Social Work

Research Proposals

A Workbook

Richard M. Grinnell, Jr.
Western Michigan University

Yvonne A. Unrau
Western Michigan University

www.PairBondPublications.com

Check Out Our Website

www.PairBondPublications.com

- √ Purchase book
- √ Templates for homework assignments
- √ Templates for writing research proposals
- √ Other online resources

Pair Bond Publications
652 Wynding Oaks
Kalamazoo, Michigan 49006
(269) 353-7100

PREFACE FOR INSTRUCTORS

Our inexpensive, highly practical book is written in a straightforward manner for social work students who are writing their first research proposals. Some students will be writing them as a part of their research methods courses, evaluation courses, administration courses, class projects, individual portfolios, capstone courses, internships, undergraduate and graduate theses, or even Ph.D. dissertations.

Our book is a primer, an introduction, a beginning. Our aim is to skim the surface of the research enterprise—to put a toe in the water, so to speak—and to give your students a taste of what it might be like to swim in the vast sea of proposal writing.

ASSUMPTIONS

We assume your students will have taken—or are now taking—a research methods course. We also assume they have some proficiency in conducting literature searches and writing literature reviews.

WHAT OUR BOOK IS ABOUT

In a nutshell, we present the basic components (via Tips) that need to be addressed in each of the 12 sections of an elementary quantitatively orientated research proposal. However, instructors and students alike can easily apply additional qualitative methodology (via additional Tips) to appropriate sections in an effort to produce mixed-methods proposals—or what are currently referred to as mixed-model proposals.

We have only provided our notion of what constitutes the rudimentary ingredients of a research proposal. We are fully aware, however, that some instructors will have different ideas about what needs to be added, subtracted, or modified in our basic ingredient list. We encourage creativeness, and urge you and your students to add, delete, and/or modify our book's content and organization to fit individual predilections.

As you can see within the pages that follow, we require students to read specific chapters in their research methods book *before* they begin writing crucial sections of their proposals. We even provide the specific pages to be read. Obviously, you can alter our suggested readings or add additional ones. Whatever the case, we firmly believe that students need to understand basic research concepts before they can competently apply them within their proposals.

It's pointless, for example, for students to start writing about how they plan to collect data without first understanding the advantages and disadvantages of the various data-collection methods. All of this content is addressed in their research methods texts. Thus, our book is designed to complement—not replace—your students' research methods book; that is, we want it to be used in *conjunction with* any social work research methods texts such as the following staples:

- Engel, R.J., & Schutt, R.K. (2014). *Fundamentals of social work research* (2nd ed.). Thousand Oaks, CA: Sage.

- Engel, R.J., & Schutt, R.K. (2012). *The practice of research in social work* (3rd ed.). Thousand Oaks, CA: Sage.

- Grinnell, R.M., Jr., & Unrau, Y.A. (Eds.). (2018). *Social work research and evaluation: Foundations of evidence-based practice* (11th ed.). New York: Oxford University Press.

- Grinnell, R.M., Jr., Williams, M., & Unrau, Y.A. (2019). *Research methods for social workers: An introduction* (12th ed.). Kalamazoo, MI: Pair Bond Publications.

- Krysik, J., & Finn, J. (2018). *Research for effective social work: New directions in social work practice* (4th ed.). New York: Routledge.

- Rubin, A., & Babbie, E.R. (2015). *Essential research methods for social work* (4th ed.). Belmont, CA: Wadsworth.

- Rubin, A., & Babbie, E.R. (2016). *Research methods for social work* (9th ed.). Belmont, CA: Brooks Cole.

HOMEWORK ASSIGNMENTS

We have provided homework assignments at the end of each section. These require your students to read various sections of published research studies that have appeared as articles in social work journals. They are contained in boxes throughout our book. Some of the assignments use unpublished research proposals as well.

ALTERNATE RESEARCH STUDIES?

You can have your students read different research studies than the ones we present in our book if you want; that is, you can easily replace our selection with yours. Or, you can let your students choose based on their own individual interests.

No matter which research study is selected, the homework assignments are all designed to provide students with a bit of experience in applying the material they have learned from your lectures, their research methods book, and our book, to actual social work research studies—ours, yours, or your students. It's up to you.

As you know, a research proposal is developed before a research project actually begins—in theory, that is. It's written—or at least thoroughly planned out in one's mind—before its implementation. We want students to write about what they think the research proposals would have looked like for published studies, given the content of their research methods book and this one. In essence, the homework assignments force students to work backward as they prepare make-believe sections of research proposals from published research studies. The homework assignments are not walks in the park and they go something like this:

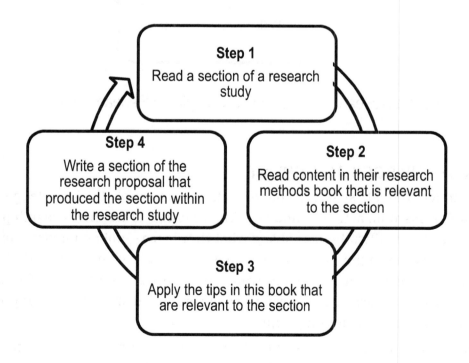

From a Completed Research Study to a Research Proposal

PROPOSAL ASSIGNMENTS

We have also included a proposal assignment at the end of each section. These will help your students to develop their own research proposals: each assignment simply requires them to write a section of their own research proposal in a systematic and highly integrated manner.

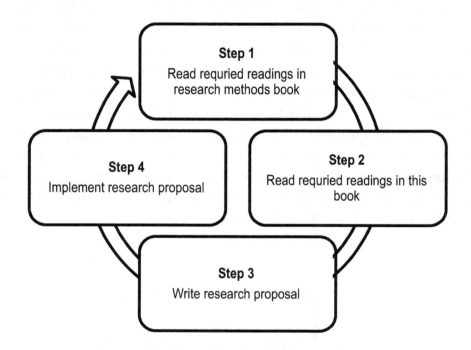

From a Research Proposal to a Completed Research Study

THINK OF OUR BOOK AS A BRIDGE

As you know, students struggle a bit when they try to apply the knowledge they gain from their classroom activities and required readings to writing research proposals; that is, they have difficulty in applying what they learn—not an uncommon occurrence. For example, your students may have read a chapter from their research methods book on various sampling strategies, have attended classes where these strategies were discussed, and perhaps even completed an individual or group assignment on some "sampling" topic.

They have acquired a lot of basic information. They now need some guidance on how to apply their newly gained expertise to writing their research proposals. They have a tendency to ask straightforward questions such as What exactly am I supposed to write about for my sample when the maximum length of the Sampling section is only one to two paragraphs at best? What content do I have to include? What can I delete? How is it written? What are some of the things I should watch out for? Are there examples I can look at?

Our book addresses these legitimate questions in a step-by-step manner. Think of our book as a bridge if you will—one that helps students to apply their knowledge to writing research proposals.

BOOK'S WEBSITE

The book's website contains content your students can use to help them with their homework assignments in addition to writing, organizing, and synthesizing their research proposals into a well-thought-out paper. The book's website contains:

- All homework assignments sorted by the 12 sections contained within research proposals. Students can complete them with an individualized template for each assignment.
- All individualized templates students can use for writing all the sections of their research proposals.
- Additional useful proposal-related resources:

Your students can then submit their completed homework assignments and competed sections of their research proposals to you via hard paper copies or through e-mails—or not at all.

A FINAL WORD

The practice of writing research proposals in our profession continues to grow and develop, and we believe our book will contribute to that growth. We are anticipating another edition down the road, and suggestions for it (e.g., additional Tips) are more than welcome. E-mail your comments directly to: rick.grinnell@wmich.edu.

Richard M. Grinnell, Jr.

Yvonne A. Unrau

PREFACE FOR STUDENTS

Writing a social work research proposal that you will be proud of takes a lot of time, so start early. Begin thinking about your research topic area well in advance of the final drop-dead date when you have to turn in your masterpiece to either your social work instructor or funding agency.

Make a habit of collecting and storing references while you are working on all sections of your proposal. Be prepared to write numerous drafts, and show them to your classmates and instructor as you go along. Make revisions based upon their feedback. Go over the language, style, and form of your proposal, after you have their feedback. Remember that your proposal will be revised many times, so plan accordingly.

If you are writing your proposal under the supervision of a social work instructor, you should seek feedback throughout your writing process, especially while selecting your research problem area and formulating a specific research question (or hypothesis)—the toughest part of a proposal to master.

It is important to note that our book presents a basic generic framework and guidelines (via Tips) for preparing the standard research proposal. Your instructor may also want you to include (or exclude) additional content in your proposal. If this is the case, you need to obtain clarification from your instructor about what you are supposed to delete, add, or modify before you start writing your first word.

In addition, your instructor may want you to read different research studies than the ones we present in our book.

WRITE YOUR NOTES DIRECTLY IN THE BOOK

We have provided ample space within our book so you can write notes as your course goes along.

YOUR PERSONAL WEBSITE

The book's website has valuable content you can use to help you write your homework assignments, in addition to helping you organize and write your research proposal. For example, it contains:

- All homework assignments categorized by the 12 sections within a proposal. You can complete all of them with an individualized template for each assignment.
- An individualized template for each of the 12 sections of your research proposal.
- Additional useful proposal-related resources:
  - Online glossary
  - Evidence-based practice links
  - Additional readings by topic

You can then submit your completed work to your instructor as hard copies or through e-mail. Use our book and its website so you can become a happy-go-lucky proposal writer.

Good luck in writing your proposal.

Richard M. Grinnell, Jr.
Yvonne A. Unrau

TABLE OF CONTENTS

PART I
Introduction to Proposal Writing

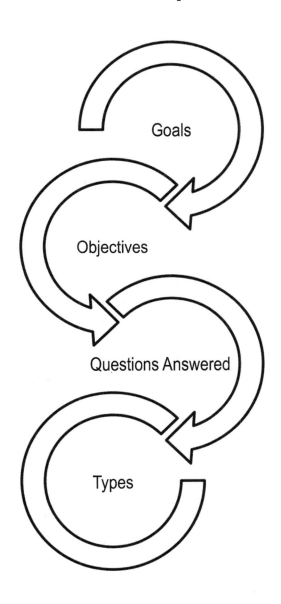

GOALS

Social work research proposals have two primary goals:

1. To receive permission from your research instructor (or thesis/dissertation committee) to do a research study. This is probably the goal that you are working on if you are currently enrolled in a social work research methods course where your instructor requires you to do a research proposal as one of the course's requirements.

   Also, you need to remember that your instructor may or may not require you to actually implement the proposal you finally write—that is, will you be required to actually carry out what you propose after your proposal is finally completed? If so, be sure to write a proposal that is realistic for your time frame, finances, and skill level.

2. To request money from a funding agency to actually carry out your research proposal.

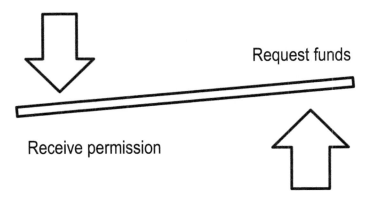

Request funds

Receive permission

Why We Write Research Proposals

OBJECTIVES

With the two goals of research proposals in mind, first-class proposals must quickly and easily respond to seven objectives. Whether you are trying to receive official permission to do a research study and/or are requesting funds to do it, you need to write a proposal that addresses seven highly integrated objectives:

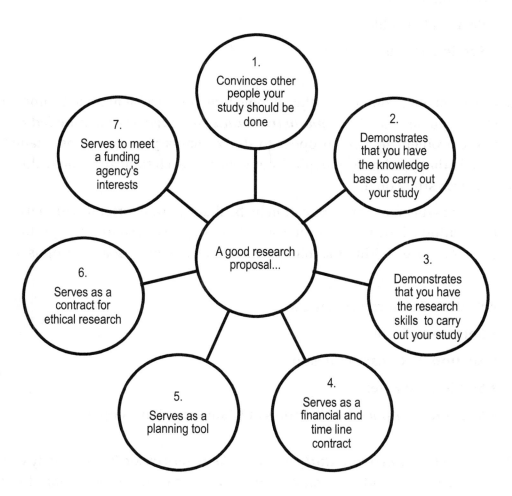

1. You must ***convince other people*** of the value, significance, and usefulness of your proposed study. These folks could be your research instructor, your classmates, your fellow researchers, the agencies that fund research endeavors, the social work agencies where your study may take place, and your educational institution.

   In a nutshell, you must show them how your proposed research study will make a difference to someone besides yourself. What difference will your study make to your university, your fellow students, the profession of social work, the state, the nation, the world, the galaxy, the universe? In other words, "who cares?" You will answer this question under the following sections within your research proposal:

   - **Section 4:** Introduction
   - **Section 6:** Problem
   - **Section 10:** Significance

2. Once you have convinced other people that your problem area is important to study, you now need to ***demonstrate that you have a solid knowledge base*** in the problem area you propose to study. That is, you need to persuade key people that you know enough about your research topic to actually do a research study on it.

   You will answer this question by brilliantly summarizing, comparing, and integrating all the relevant theory and existing research findings pertaining to your topic area within the following sections of your research proposal:

   - **Section 5:** Literature Review
   - **Section 6:** Problem
   - **Section 7:** Research Question
   - **Section 11:** References
   - **Section 12:** Appendix M: Copies of Résumés of Key People

3. You must ***demonstrate that you have the research skills*** to actually carry out your proposed study. You may know a lot about your research topic, but do

you have the skills to carry it out? Simply put, you do this by writing a well-thought-out, practical, and feasible research proposal that clearly outlines how you plan to obtain and analyze the data your study will collect. These data will then answer your research question (or test your hypothesis).

Will your collected data be reliable and valid—and more importantly—will the data really be able to answer your research question (or test your hypothesis)? You will answer these questions under the following sections within your research proposal:

- **Section 8:** Method
  - o **Section 8a:** Research Design
  - o **Section 8b:** Sample
  - o **Section 8c:** Instrumentation
  - o **Section 8d:** Data Collection
  - o **Section 8e:** Data Analysis
- **Section 9:** Limitations

4. Your proposal will ***serve as a financial and time-line contract***. Research projects sometimes involve contracts between several individuals or groups. Your research proposal should state clearly what each party is expected to bring to your research project, how you will use financial and human resources, and when your study will be completed. How much will your research study cost and how long will it take? You will answer these questions under the following section within your research proposal:

- **Section 12**: Appendixes
  - o Appendix A: Letter(s) of permission
  - o Appendix B: Cooperating agency description
  - o Appendix C: Time line
  - o Appendix O: Budget

5. The proposal also will ***serve as a comprehensive planning tool.*** Many research projects fail because they were not properly planned from the outset. When badly planned studies finally reach their conclusion, it is typically very stressful for the researchers. When a clear plan of action is in place from the beginning, the study is more likely to proceed smoothly to a successful conclusion than a vague, hazy, and fuzzy study that was planned at the last minute. All these concerns are addressed throughout your entire proposal.

6. The proposal will ***serve as contract for engaging in ethical research practices.*** Will you be doing research on humans? If so, what safeguards are you putting in place so you don't hurt them? You will answer these questions under the following sections within your research proposal:

- **Section 8b:** Sample
- **Section 8c:** Instrumentation
- **Section 8d:** Data Collection
- **Section 12:** Appendixes
  o **Appendix E:** Consent Form
  o **Appendix F:** Assent Form
  o **Appendix G:** Institutional Review Board Approval

7. How does your proposed study ***relate to the funding agency's interests?*** This question is best answered in the cover letter you attach to your finished research proposal. You must highlight how your proposal is directly related and relevant to the agency's basic interests. This will not be an issue for you if you're not asking for funds to do your study.

Some funding agencies provide detailed instructions or guidelines concerning the preparation of research proposals (and, in some cases, forms on which they are to be typed); obviously, you must carefully read these guidelines *before* you begin to write your first sentence.

TYPES

On a general level, there are six types of research proposals:

1. ***Social work students' classroom research proposals.*** This type of proposal is probably the one that you are writing. It is used to demonstrate your knowledge of the complete social work research process, from selecting a research topic to study to disseminating the results from the study.

2. ***Solicited proposals.*** These proposals are submitted in response to specific solicitations issued by potential funding agencies. These solicitations, typically called Request for Proposals (RFP), are usually very specific in their requirements regarding what types of research problems areas they are willing to fund, in addition to providing the proposal's format, style, and level of detail.

3. ***Unsolicited proposals.*** These proposals are submitted to potential funding agencies that have not issued specific solicitations but are believed by the researchers to have interests in their research problem areas.

4. ***Preproposals.*** These are requested when potential funding sponsors wish to minimize applicants' efforts in preparing full-blown proposals. Preproposals are usually in the form of "letters of intent." After preproposals are reviewed, the funding agencies notify potential investigators if they should submit full proposals.

5. ***Continuation or noncompeting proposals.*** These types of proposals simply request continued funding of multiyear projects for which the sponsors have already provided funding for initial periods (normally one year). Continued financial support is usually contingent on satisfactory work progress and the availability of funds.

6. ***Renewal or competing proposals.*** These types of proposals request continued support for existing projects that are about to terminate. From the sponsors' viewpoint, these generally have the same status as unsolicited proposals.

9

PART II
Front Matter

Sections 1–4 in a research proposal are usually written last—that is, after you have completed the other eight sections (Sections 5–12). However, they are presented first in our book so that you can jot down some initial ideas and revise these sections as your proposal develops over time.. Note that the first three sections of a research proposal are called the "Front Matter." The fourth section actually begins the "guts" of your research proposal.

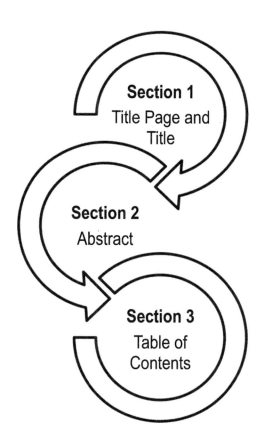

TITLE PAGE AND TITLE

(1 page) (< 12 words)

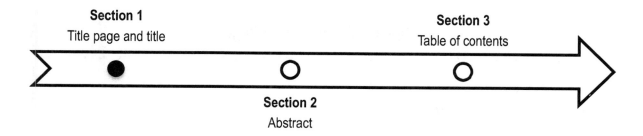

Section 1
Title page and title

Section 3
Table of contents

Section 2
Abstract

Front Matter of a Research Proposal

Your proposal's title will change many times as you write the remaining sections of your research proposal. Think of your title as "a working title." So be prepared to change your title as time goes on!

When writing your title, reexamine your research purposes, questions, or hypotheses to identify your main variables. These should be referred to in your title. The example below shows the purpose of a simple social work research proposal and a suggested corresponding title.

Example

Research purpose: The purpose of this research study is to explore the relationship between administrative styles of social work supervisors and the effectiveness and efficiency of their supervisees.

Corresponding title: The Relationship between the Administrative Styles of Social Work Supervisors and the Effectiveness and Efficiency of Their Supervisees

After you have successfully completed your research study you will need to disseminate your study's findings by submitting a manuscript for possible publication to a professional social work journal. The title of your research proposal will be very similar—if not exact—to the title of the manuscript you finally submit for possible publication.

		Tips for Writing a Title Page
#		**Tips**
1	**Yes No** ☺ ☹	Check to see if your research instructor (or funding agency you have in mind) has any specifications for your Title/Cover Page.
2	**Yes No** ☺ ☹	Check to be sure you included the names of key people who will be affiliated with your project. Usually the Title/Cover Page includes the people who will be involved in your proposed research study (e.g., Department Head, your research supervisor, your research instructor, Contracts Officer, Executive Director of the social work agency that your study will take place). Thus, if your proposed research study involves collaboration with other groups/organizations, it's a good idea to include their names on your Title/Cover Page.

3	**Yes** **No** 🙂 🙁	Check to see if your Title Page looks professional and neat. However, do not waste time using fancy report covers, expensive binding, or other procedures that may send the wrong message to your potential funding agency. You are trying to impress them with how you really need funding, not the message that you do things rather expensively!
4	**Yes** **No** 🙂 🙁	Check with your research instructor to see if he/she has any examples of title pages from other research proposals to show you.

Tips for Writing a Title

#		**Tips**
5	**Yes** **No** 🙂 🙁	Check to see if the title of your study is comprehensive enough to clearly indicate the nature of your proposed project. Your title should make sense standing all by itself.
6	**Yes** **No** 🙂 🙁	Check to see if your title is logical, brief, and descriptive. It should not contain more than 20 words—the shorter the better.
7	**Yes** **No** 🙂 🙁	Check to see if your title contains the important variables that you propose to study.
8	**Yes** **No** 🙂 🙁	Check to see that your title is not a sentence and does not end with a period. If your title is getting too long, try removing some words. When all else fails, try using a two-part title with the parts separated by a colon (use only as a last resort!).

9	Yes No	Check to see if you avoided the temptation to put the anticipated results of your study in the title.
10	Yes No	Check to see if your title is concise and unambiguous. Resist trying to make it "cute."
11	Yes No	Check to see if your title contains specific, familiar, and short words.
12	Yes No	Check to see if your title is understandable and jargon-free.
13	Yes No	Check to see if your title paints a quick overall picture of the key idea(s) that you propose to study.
14	Yes No	Check to see if your title mentions the sample or population (research participants) you wish to study.
15	Yes No	Check to see that your title does not contain abbreviations.
16	Yes No	Check to see that your title contains the correct syntax (word order). The words you use in your title should clearly reflect the focus of your proposal. The most important words should come first, then the less important words. Try to remove words from your title that really are not necessary for understanding.
17	Yes No	Check with your research instructor to see if he/she has any examples of titles from other research proposals to show you.

Section 1
Writing a Title for Your Research Proposal

Write a *tentative* title for your research proposal in the white space provided below. The box will expand as you type.

- Use all the tips in this section to write your title (e.g., be sure it's not a sentence and doesn't end with a period).
- If possible, show your title to your classmates for their feedback.
- Revise your title based on your classmates' feedback.
- Submit your title to your instructor for comments.

NOTE: As you know, you won't write the final version of your title until after you have completed Sections 5–12 of your research proposal. Thus, it is important for you to remember that at this point in the proposal-writing process your title should be considered a draft, which will transform into a masterpiece as your proposal develops over the semester.

Your Name(s):

Your Identification Number(s) (if any):

Type your *tentative* Title section here.
(Box will automatically expand as you type)

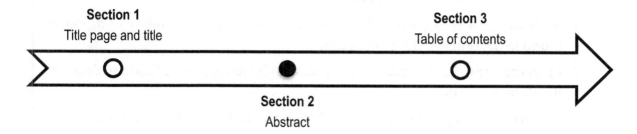

Front Matter of a Research Proposal

Potential funders use abstracts to make initial decisions about whether they are interested in providing financial support for the proposals they receive. Reviewers, who usually read a high number of proposals, obtain their initial impressions by reading abstracts, thereby making abstracts a significant aspect of the review process.

An abstract is a summary that provides an overview of the proposal. When there are many competing proposals (such as for research funding), preparing a good abstract is exceedingly important because some reviewers may eliminate certain proposals based on their abstracts alone. For instance, if the funding agency is concentrating on pregnant adolescents and your abstract fails to mention this group, it may not get further consideration.

Generally, your abstract synthesizes the body of your proposal. While limiting the maximum number of words to between 200 and 250, you must clearly and concisely state your research question (or hypothesis), outline the means you'll use to answer that question (or test your hypothesis), and indicate your anticipated results and their significance to the social work profession. Just as we mentioned in the section about your title page (Section 1), your abstract will be refined over time and will be finally written after Sections 5–12 have been fully completed.

For many academic purposes (such as a term project), a short abstract (say, 200–250 words) is adequate. You should check your institution or instructor's requirements regarding your abstract's length. Use the following four subheadings if you are writing a short abstract:

Short Abstract

1. ***Purpose (or objective) of the study.*** The material for this subheading can be found in Section 7: Research Question.

2. ***Method(s) used to gather the data.*** The material for this subheading can be found in Section 8d: Data Collection.

3. ***Projected results.*** The material for this subheading can be found in Section 8e: Data Analysis.

4. ***Implications of projected results.*** The material for this subheading can be found in Section 10: Significance.

Longer abstracts simply need numerous subheadings to guide readers such as:

Long Abstract

1. ***Problem area*** (including importance). The material for this subheading can be found in Section 6: Problem.

2. ***Research purpose*** (or question or hypothesis). The material for this subheading can be found in Section 7: Research Question.

3. ***Related literature*** (brief overview of most salient aspects). The material for this subheading can be found in Section 5: Literature Review.

4. ***Research participants*** (including sampling plan). The material for this subheading can be found in Section 8b: Sample.

5. ***Instrumentation*** (types of instruments that will be used; names of instruments are usually not needed in the abstract). The material for this subheading can be found in Section 8c: Instrumentation.

6. ***Methods of data collection.*** The material for this subheading can be found in Section 8d: Data Collection.

7. ***Method of data analysis*** (descriptive and inferential, if any, or type of qualitative analysis). The material for this subheading can be found in Section 8e: Data Analysis.

8. ***Potential implications.*** The material for this subheading can be found in Section 10: Implications.

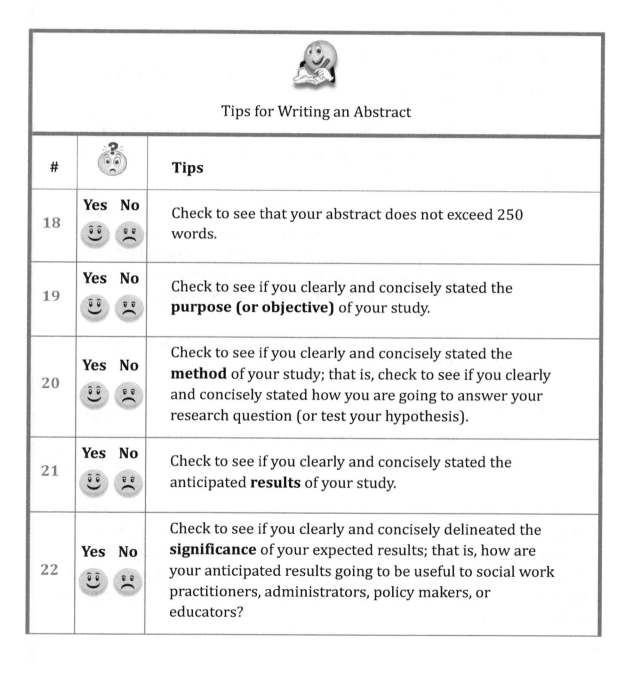

Tips for Writing an Abstract

#		Tips
18	**Yes No**	Check to see that your abstract does not exceed 250 words.
19	**Yes No**	Check to see if you clearly and concisely stated the **purpose (or objective)** of your study.
20	**Yes No**	Check to see if you clearly and concisely stated the **method** of your study; that is, check to see if you clearly and concisely stated how you are going to answer your research question (or test your hypothesis).
21	**Yes No**	Check to see if you clearly and concisely stated the anticipated **results** of your study.
22	**Yes No**	Check to see if you clearly and concisely delineated the **significance** of your expected results; that is, how are your anticipated results going to be useful to social work practitioners, administrators, policy makers, or educators?

23	Yes No	Check to see that you included "key words" at the bottom of your abstract.
24	Yes No	Check to see that you clearly defined all abbreviations (except units of measurements), acronyms, and unique terms.
25	Yes No	Check to see that your abstract reports accurate information that is in the body of the accompanying proposal.
26	Yes No	Check to see if your abstract is extraordinarily clear to the common reader. Do not try to impress your friends with fancy words.
27	Yes No	Check to see if you included enough relevant material to provide the ingredients that are needed for all four criteria that are usually required for abstracts that appear in professional social work journal articles: (1) purpose, (2) method, (3) results, and (4) implications.
28	Yes No	Check to see if you wrote your abstract in the future tense.
29	Yes No	Check with your research instructor to see if he/she has any examples of proposal abstracts to show you.

After you have successfully completed your research study, you will need to disseminate your study's findings by submitting a manuscript for possible publication to a professional social work journal. The abstract of your research proposal should be very similar to the abstract of the manuscript you submit for possible publication.

Boxes 2.1 and 2.2 provide two examples of abstracts for articles that appeared in a professional social work journal. Note how the contents of the published abstracts are very similar to the ones for research proposals. The major difference between the two is that abstracts for research proposals are written in the future tense whereas abstracts for manuscripts that are submitted for possible publication are written in the present tense, as illustrated in Box 2.2. However, once in a while you will see published abstracts written in past tense, as demonstrated in Boxes 2.1 and 2.2.

BOX 2.1

Example of an Abstract from an Article That Appeared in a Professional Journal

**Evaluating Culturally Responsive Group Work
with Black Women[1]**

Purpose: This study examined the efficacy of a culturally congruent group treatment model, entitled "Claiming Your Connections" (CYC) aimed at reducing depressive symptoms and perceived stress, and enhancing psychosocial competence (i.e., locus of control and active coping) among Black women. **Method:** A total of 58 Black women recruited from health and human service community-based organizations were randomly assigned to either the CYC intervention or a wait-list control group. Women in the CYC program attended weekly group intervention sessions over a 10-week period, and the wait-list control group did not receive any treatment for the same duration. **Results:** At pretreatment both groups indicated moderate levels of depressive symptoms, perceived stress, and psychosocial competence. After the intervention, the CYC group reported a significant reduction in depressive symptoms and perceived stress. There was no statistically significant change on these variables for the control group. **Implications:** Results suggest that the CYC group intervention program is effective with Black women who report having difficulty managing stressors of daily life.

---

[1]Jones, L.V., & Warner, L.A. (2011). Evaluating culturally responsive group work with Black women. *Research on Social Work Practice, 21*, 737–746.

BOX 2.2

Example of an Abstract from an Article That Appeared in a Professional Journal

Therapist Effects on Disparities Experienced by Minorities Receiving Services for Mental Illness[1]

Objectives: The authors examine if some of the reason clients from racial and ethnic minority groups experience outcome disparities is explained by their therapists. **Method:** Data from 98 clients (19% minority) and 14 therapists at two community mental health agencies where clients from racial and ethnic minority groups were experiencing outcome disparities were analyzed using hierarchical linear modeling with treatment outcomes at Level 1, client factors at Level 2, and therapists at Level 3. **Results:** There were substantial therapist effects that moderated the relationship between clients' race and treatment outcomes (outcome disparities). Therapists accounted for 28.7% of the variability in outcome disparities. **Conclusions:** Therapists are linked to outcome disparities and appear to play a substantial role in why disparities occur.

---

[1]Larrison, C.R., & Schoppelrey, S.L. (2011). Therapist effects on disparities experienced by minorities receiving services for mental illness. *Research on Social Work Practice, 21,* 727–736.

   Homework Assignment 2.1

Writing *Short* Abstracts for Research Proposals

Box 2.1 presents an abstract from a social work journal article. Download and read the article. Now that you are familiar with the research study depicted in Box 2.1:

In the white space below, write a *short* hypothetical abstract you feel the authors *should have* written for the research proposal their study was based upon. The box will expand as you type.

NOTE: You do not have a copy of the authors' research proposal. You only have a copy of the article that resulted from the implementation of their proposal. Your main objective is to edit, revise, rearrange, and/or modify the authors' published abstract as you think it *should have* appeared in their research proposal.

* Use all the tips in this section to write your hypothetical proposal abstract (e.g., contains four subsections, written in future tense).
* Submit your revised Abstract section to your instructor, pointing out all the revisions you made and why you made them.

Your Name(s):
Your Identification Number(s) (if any):
Assignment 2.1

Type your short Abstract section here.
(Box will automatically expand as you type)

Homework Assignment 2.2

Writing *Short* Abstracts for Research Proposals

Box 2.2 presents an abstract from a social work journal article. Download and read the article. Now that you are familiar with the research study depicted in Box 2.2:

In the white space below, write a *short* hypothetical abstract you feel the authors *should have* written for the research proposal their study was based upon. The box will expand as you type.

NOTE: You do not have a copy of the authors' research proposal. You only have a copy of the article that resulted from the implementation of their proposal. Your main objective is to edit, revise, rearrange, and/or modify the authors' published abstract as you think it *should have* appeared in their research proposal.

- Use all the tips in this section to write your hypothetical proposal abstract (e.g., contains four subsections, written in future tense).
- Submit your revised Abstract section to your instructor, pointing out all the revisions you made and why you made them.

Your Name(s):
Your Identification Number(s) (if any):
Assignment 2.2

Type your short Abstract section here.
(Box will automatically expand as you type)

   **Homework Assignment 2.3**

Writing *Long* Abstracts for Research Proposals

Box 2.1 presents an abstract from a social work journal article. Download and read the article. Now that you are familiar with the research study depicted in Box 2.1:

In the white space below, write a *long* hypothetical abstract you feel the authors *should have* written for the research proposal their study was based upon. The box will expand as you type.

NOTE: You do not have a copy of the authors' research proposal. You only have a copy of the article that resulted from the implementation of their proposal. Your main objective is to edit, revise, rearrange, and/or modify the authors' published abstract as you think it *should have* appeared in their research proposal.

- Use all the tips in this section to write your hypothetical proposal abstract (e.g., contains four subsections, written in future tense).
- Submit your revised Abstract section to your instructor, pointing out all the revisions you made and why you made them.

Your Name(s):
Your Identification Number(s) (if any):
Assignment 2.3

Type your long Abstract section here.
(Box will automatically expand as you type)

 Homework Assignment 2.4

Writing *Long* Abstracts for Research Proposals

Box 2.2 presents an abstract from a social work journal article. Download and read the article. Now that you are familiar with the research study depicted in Box 2.2:

In the white space below, write a *long* hypothetical abstract you feel the authors *should have* written for the research proposal their study was based upon. The box will expand as you type.

NOTE: You do not have a copy of the authors' research proposal. You only have a copy of the article that resulted from the implementation of their proposal. Your main objective is to edit, revise, rearrange, and/or modify the authors' published abstract as you think it *should have* appeared in their research proposal.

- Use all the tips in this section to write your hypothetical proposal abstract (e.g., contains four subsections, written in future tense).
- Submit your revised Abstract section to your instructor, pointing out all the revisions you made and why you made them.

Your Name(s):
Your Identification Number(s) (if any):
Assignment 2.4

Type your long Abstract section here.
(Box will automatically expand as you type)

Section 2
Writing a Short Abstract for Your Research Proposal

Write a *short* abstract for your research proposal in the white space provided below. The box will expand as you type.

- Use all the tips in this section to write your abstract (e.g., contains four subsections, written in future tense).
- If possible, show your abstract to your classmates for their feedback.
- Revise your abstract based on your classmates' feedback.
- Submit your abstract to your instructor for comments.

NOTE: As you know, you will actually write the *final version* of your abstract after you have completed Sections 5–12 of your research proposal. Thus, it is important for you to remember that at this point in the proposal-writing process your abstract should be considered a draft, which will transform into a masterpiece as your proposal develops over the semester.

Your Name(s):

Your Identification Number(s) (if any):

Title of Your Research Proposal:

Type your short Abstract section here.

(Box will automatically expand as you type)

TABLE OF CONTENTS
(1 page)

Section 3

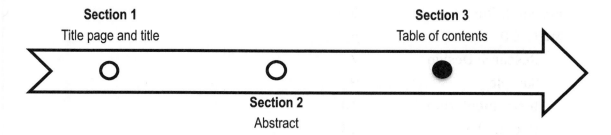

Section 1
Title page and title

Section 3
Table of contents

Section 2
Abstract

Front Matter of a Research Proposal

A short research proposal with few parts does not need a table of contents. However, a longer and more detailed proposal may require not only a table of contents but a list of illustrations, figures, graphs, and tables as well.

Your Table of Contents section (along with your title and abstract) is finalized after you have completed Sections 4–12. On the following page is an example of the Table of Contents for a typical social work research proposal:

PART III
Identifying the Problem

This portion of your research proposal is all about introducing your readers to the general problem area you want to study and letting them know the specific research question you want to answer or hypothesis you want to test.

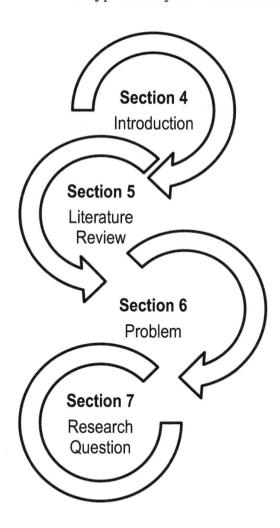

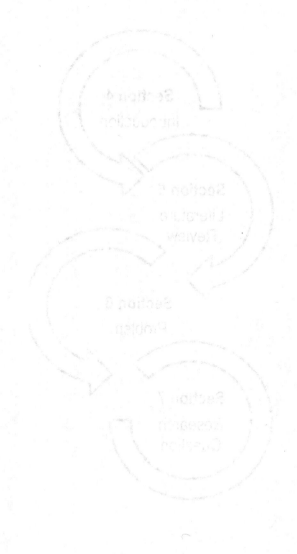

INTRODUCTION

(2–3 pages)

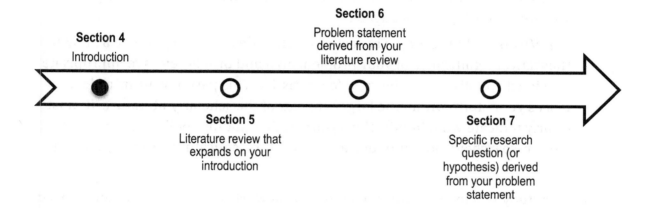

Section 4
Introduction

Section 6
Problem statement
derived from your
literature review

Section 5
Literature review that
expands on your
introduction

Section 7
Specific research
question (or
hypothesis) derived
from your problem
statement

Identifying the Problem

The Introduction section of your research proposal will contain three distinct subsections. Write your short Introduction section in this specific order:

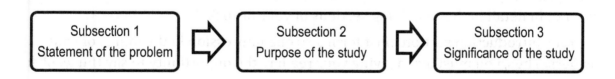

Subsection 1
Statement of the problem

Subsection 2
Purpose of the study

Subsection 3
Significance of the study

1. ***Statement of the problem.*** The first part of your Introduction section should begin with a succinct statement of what general problem area you are proposing to study. You need to briefly describe the major issues that your proposed research study will address and lay the broad foundation for the problem area that leads to your proposed study.

2. ***Purpose of the study.*** The second part provides a brief background of your problem area to enable an informed layperson to place your particular research problem in a context of common knowledge. In a nutshell, this subsection points out why your particular study is needed. This can be done in a number of ways. For example, you might be able to point out that various government agencies and/or prominent scholars have called for additional research in the problem area you wish to investigate further. You might also mention some statistics showing that the problem area affects many people you are proposing to investigate.

3. ***Significance of the study.*** The last subsection describes the practical and/or theoretical significance of your problem area and briefly refers to appropriate previously published studies and/or statistics. This part of your Introduction places your study within the larger context of the scholarly literature. It must clearly indicate what implications your study's findings will have for social work researchers, practitioners, administrators, educators, or policy makers.

If your study will involve working with a social work agency that also sees a need for your study, you need to include this information in this section and put a copy of the support letter written by the agency's Executive Director in an appendix (e.g., Appendix B in this book).

Your Introduction section needs to provide your readers with a broad overview of your proposal—a snapshot, if you will. This will show them the overall picture of what you are trying to do before they begin reading the specific details of exactly what you are going to do and how you are going to do it. All of these particulars are covered in detail in the remaining sections of your proposal.

Your Introduction section must form a strong impression in the minds of your readers. Thus, you must avoid giving your readers the opportunity to say things like:

- Not an original idea.
- Rationale is weak.
- Writing is vague.
- Uncertain what is to be accomplished.
- Problem area is not important.
- Looks like the proposed study is unfocused, too large, or unrealistic.

Tips for Writing an Introduction

#		Tips
30	**Yes** **No**	Check to see that your Introduction section contains the three subsections in this order: (1) statement of the problem, (2) purpose of the study, and (3) significance of the study.
31	**Yes** **No**	Check to see if you have "painted an overall descriptive picture" of your proposal in the minds of your readers.
32	**Yes** **No**	Check to see that you have established a good argument for the importance of your problem area and why your study needs to be done.
33	**Yes** **No**	Check to see that you have adequately described any underlying theories (if any) that you used to establish your problem area.
34	**Yes** **No**	Check to see that you have provided a clear and concise overview of your proposed research methodology and data analysis plans.
35	**Yes** **No**	Check to see if this section is written like an Executive Summary (the busy executive probably only has enough time to read your Introduction—not the entire proposal).

36	**Yes** 🙂	**No** ☹️	Check to see that the purpose of your proposed study clearly states your real intention. Does the purpose of your study break the problem area down into subsections for analysis?
37	**Yes** 🙂	**No** ☹️	Check to see if this section is specific and concise. Do not go into detail on aspects of your proposal that are further clarified at a later point in your proposal.
38	**Yes** 🙂	**No** ☹️	Check to see if you displayed your knowledge of the organization from which you are requesting funds (if any). Key concerns of a potential funding organization can be briefly identified in relation to your proposed project.
39	**Yes** 🙂	**No** ☹️	Check to see that your potential funding agency is committed to the same needs/problems that your proposal addresses. Clearly indicate how addressing the problems in your study helps your potential funding agency to fulfill its mission. Always keep the funding agency (or your research instructor) in your mind as a "cooperating partner" committed to the same concerns that you are. Recognizing them at the very beginning of your proposal can assist in strengthening their collaboration.
40	**Yes** 🙂	**No** ☹️	Check to see that you have avoided personal pronouns, subjective language, and awkward grammar.
41	**Yes** 🙂	**No** ☹️	Check to see that this section moves the reader, like a "funnel," from a general to a specific view of the problem area you propose to study.
42	**Yes** 🙂	**No** ☹️	Check to see that the problem area you propose to study is stated clearly, tersely, and objectively.

43	Yes 😊 No 🙁	Check to see that your research problem is stated in the proper format (e.g., relationship between variables or difference between groups).
44	Yes 😊 No 🙁	Check to see that the literature you refer to is really a true "synthesis," rather than a review, summary, or report. Also, check to see that it moves from topic to topic rather than from citation to citation.
45	Yes 😊 No 🙁	Check to be sure that this section is no more than two to three typed, double-spaced pages in length.

The Introduction section that is written for a research proposal can easily be used for the Introduction section of the manuscript you finally submit for possible publication. Boxes 4.1 and 4.2 provide examples of Introduction sections for two articles that appeared in a professional social work journal. The Introduction sections in both published examples are identical to the ones that were contained in their respective research proposals.

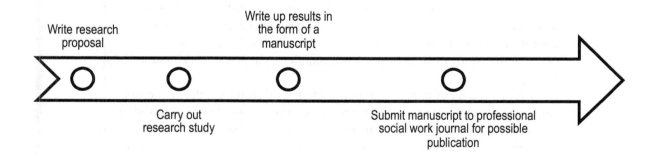

From Research Proposal to Publication

BOX 4.1

Example of an Introduction Section from an Article That Appeared in a Professional Journal

Readiness for College Engagement among Students Who Have Aged Out of Foster Care[1]

INTRODUCTION

There were over 423,000 children living in foster-care placements on any given day in the United States in 2009. Of these, over 32,000 exited the foster care system by "aging out" to independence (Child Welfare Information Gateway, 2011). Aging out is a legal event that occurs when the court formally discharges a young person from the state's custody based on the youth's chronological age. In most states, foster youth are discharged at 18 years of age; however, an increasing number of states are extending care to 21 years old as a result of the Fostering Connections to Success and Increasing Adoptions Act of 2008.

Previous research studies have indicated that most aged-out youth leaving foster care do so in unprepared and unplanned ways, and many either return to their families who were judged unfit by the court or begin living on their own (McMillen & Tucker, 1999). Upon aging-out of the system, these youth are abruptly initiated into adulthood and must rely heavily on their limited personal resources and income for their very survival (Iglehart, 1995).

Young people who have lived in foster care are less able to depend on family members for shelter, adult guidance, and financial support after high school than non-foster youth (Iglehart, 1995; Courtney, Dworsky, Lee, & Rapp, 2010). Educational attainment for foster youth lags far behind their non-foster-care peers, with just over half of foster youth completing high school (Wolanin, 2005; Sheehy et al., 2000).

Though estimates of high-school completion for foster youth vary across studies, the average of estimates suggests that approximately half of the youth between the ages of 18 and 24 who have aged out of foster care have high-school diplomas or general educational development (GED) diplomas in comparison to over 70 percent of non-foster youth (Wolanin, 2005). Other studies have found higher estimates of high-school achievement for foster youth, particularly when students attaining their GEDs are counted (Pecora et al., 2005).

This disparity has obvious implications for college entrance. Only 15 percent of foster youth are likely to enroll in college-preparatory classes during high school, whereas 32 percent of non-foster youth enroll in a high-school curriculum that helps to prepare them for college (Casey Family Programs, 2003).

Additionally, while college is a possible next step after high school, students growing up in foster care receive few encouraging messages from educators, social workers, and other adults regarding the pursuit of a college education (Davis, 2006). Only 20 percent of college-qualified foster youth attend college compared to 60 percent of their non-foster-care peers (Wolanin, 2005). Similarly, degree completion for foster youth, with estimates ranging from a low of 1 percent to a high of 10.8 percent, is substantially lower than the 24 percent degree-completion rate of non-foster youth (Pecora et al., 2006; Wolanin, 2005).

Research has generally suggested more negative outcomes for former foster youth compared to the general population, including disproportionate representation in the adult homeless population (Park, Metraux, & Culhane, 2005) as well as increased rates of unemployment and lack of health insurance (Reilly, 2003), mental illness (Courtney & Dworsky, 2006), and involvement in the criminal justice system (McMillen, Vaughn, & Shook, 2008).

In response to these dismal trajectories, federal legislation has provided monies to states to pay for services to help with the transition out of foster care into some form of independent living. For example, the Foster Care Independence Act of 1999 provides funding ($140 million) to state governments to improve and expand their current independent-living programs for foster youth who age out of the system.

The Promoting Safe and Stable Families Amendment of 2001 enhances the Foster Care Independence Act by providing additional funding ($60 million) for payments to state governments for post-secondary education and training. This funding pays for the Educational Training Voucher (ETV) program, which provides up to $5,000 per year up to age 23 for foster youth enrolled in post-secondary education as long as they enroll in the ETV program prior to 21 years of age.

The Fostering Connection to Success and Increasing Adoptions Act of 2008 permits states to claim federal reimbursement for foster-care maintenance payments made on behalf of foster youth to age 21. Foster youth living in states that take advantage of this policy and extend care can benefit by voluntarily remaining in the state's custody.

REFERENCES

Child Welfare Information Gateway. (2011). *Foster care statistics 2009*. Washington, DC: U.S. Department of Health and Human Services, Children's Bureau. Retrieved on June 7, 2011 from: http://www.childwelfare.gov/pubs/factsheets/foster.cfm

Courtney, M., Dworsky, A., Lee, J., & Raap, M. (2010). *Midwest evaluation of the adult functioning of former foster youth: Outcomes at ages 23 and 24*. Chicago: Chapin Hall Center for Children at the University of Chicago.

Iglehart, A.P. (1995). Readiness for independence: Comparison of foster care, kinship care, and non-foster care adolescents. *Children and Youth Services Review, 17*, 417–432.

McMillen, J.C. & Tucker, J. (1999). The status of older adolescents at exit from out-of-home care, *Child Welfare, 78*, 339–360.

McMillen, J.C., Vaughn, M.G., & Shook, J.J. (2008). Aging out of foster care and legal involvement: Toward a typology of risk. *Social Service Review, 82*, 419–446.

Park, J.M., Metraux, S., & Culhane, D.P. (2005). Childhood out-of-home placement and dynamics of public shelter utilization among young homeless adults. *Children and Youth Services Review, 27*, 533–546.

Pecora, P.J., Williams, J., Kessler, R.C., Hiripi, E., O'Brien, K., Emerson, J., Herrick, M.A., & Torres, D. (2006). Assessing the educational achievements of adults who were formerly placed in family foster care. *Child & Family Social Work, 11*, 220–231.

Reilly, T. (2003). Transition from care: Status and outcomes of youth who age out of foster care. *Child Welfare, 82*, 727–746.

Wolanin, T.R. (2005*). Higher education opportunities for foster youth: A primer for policymakers.* Washington, DC: Institute for Higher Education Policy.

----

[1]Unrau, Y.A., Font, S.A., & Rawls, G. (2012). Readiness for college engagement among students who have aged out of foster care. *Children and Youth Services Review, 34*, 76–83.

BOX 4.2

Example of an Introduction Section from an Article That Appeared in a Professional Journal

Exploring Out-of-Home Placement as a Moderator of Help Seeking Behavior among Adolescents Who Are High Risk[1]

Children placed in foster care are vulnerable to long-term physical and mental health problems owing to maltreatment and other trauma such as family separation. Many youth "age out" of foster care without high school diplomas or prospects of employment, leaving them unprepared for daily life as young adults.

Although adults with childhood foster care experience have been reported to fare less well on several social indicators such as educational achievement, community involvement, marital satisfaction, and occupational accomplishments, the reasons for their poor socialization may have as much to do with risks of poverty and family dysfunctions, as with risks associated with out-of-home placement (Buehler, Orme, Post, & Patterson, 2000). Research studies have not yet teased out which aspects of the foster care or group care experience, if any, are associated with long-term health and well-being.

Child welfare agencies play a significant role in the provision of mental health services while children live in out-of-home care (Kellam, Branch, Brown, & Russell, 1981). When children exit from foster care they often become ineligible for the various services that were once associated with their placements and must then seek help from other systems, such as schools, churches, medical clinics, families, and friends. How well the foster care or group care experience prepares children—adolescents in particular—to seek professional help for their own needs is not yet fully known. Thus, the current study investigated whether a placement experience in either foster care or group care increased the likelihood of youth seeking professional help outside of the child welfare system for a variety of physical and mental health problems.

REFERENCES

Buehler, C., Orme, J.G., Post, J., & Patterson, D. A. (2000). The long term correlates of family foster care. *Children and Youth Services Review, 22,* 595–625.

Kellam, S., Branch, J., Brown, C., & Russell, G. (1981). Why teenagers come for treatment. *Journal of the American Academy of Child and Adolescent Psychiatry, 20,* 477–495.

---

[1] Unrau, Y.A., & Grinnell, R.M., Jr. (2005). Exploring out-of-home placement as a moderator of help-seeking behavior among adolescents who are high risk. *Research on Social Work Practice, 6,* 516–530.

 | Homework Assignment 4.1 |

Writing Introduction Sections for Research Proposals

Box 4.1 presents an Introduction section from a social work journal article. Download and read the article. Now that you are familiar with the research study depicted in Box 4.1:

In the white space below, write an Introduction section you feel the authors *should have* written for the research proposal their study was based upon. The box will expand as you type.

NOTE: You do not have a copy of the authors' research proposal. You only have a copy of the article that resulted from the implementation of their proposal. Your main objective is to edit, revise, rearrange, and/or modify the authors' published Introduction section as you think it *should have* appeared in their research proposal.

• Use all the tips in this section to write your hypothetical proposal's Introduction section (e.g., contains three distinct subsections).

• Submit your revised Introduction section to your instructor, pointing out all the revisions you made and why you made them.

Your Name(s):
Your Identification Number(s) (if any):
Assignment 4.1

Type your Introduction section here.
(Box will automatically expand as you type)

Homework Assignment 4.2

Writing Introduction Sections for Research Proposals

Box 4.2 presents an Introduction section from a social work journal article. Download and read the article. Now that you are familiar with the research study depicted in Box 4.2:

In the white space below, write an Introduction section you feel the authors *should have* written for the research proposal their study was based upon. The box will expand as you type.

NOTE: You do not have a copy of the authors' research proposal. You only have a copy of the article that resulted from the implementation of their proposal. Your main objective is to edit, revise, rearrange, and/or modify the authors' published Introduction section as you think it *should have* appeared in their research proposal.

- Use all the tips in this section to write your hypothetical proposal's Introduction section (e.g., contains three distinct subsections).
- Submit your revised Introduction section to your instructor, pointing out all the revisions you made and why you made them.

Your Name(s):
Your Identification Number(s) (if any):
Assignment 4.2

Type your Introduction section here.
(Box will automatically expand as you type)

Section 4
Writing an Introduction Section for Your Research Proposal

Write an Introduction section for your research proposal in the white space provided below. The box will expand as you type.

- Use all the tips in this section to write your Introduction (e.g., contains three subsections).

- If possible, show your proposal's title (Section 1), abstract (Section 2), and your Introduction section (Section 4) to your classmates for their feedback.

- Revise your Introduction section based on your classmates' feedback.

- Submit your Title, Abstract, and Introduction sections to your instructor for comments.

NOTE: As you know, you will actually write the *final version* of your Introduction section after you have completed Sections 5–12 of your research proposal. Thus, it is important for you to remember at this point in the proposal-writing process that your Introduction section should be considered a draft, which will transform into a masterpiece as your proposal develops over the semester.

Your Name(s):
Your Identification Number(s) (if any):
Title of Your Research Proposal:
Abstract:

Type your Introduction section here.
(Box will automatically expand as you type)

LITERATURE REVIEW

(5–7 pages)

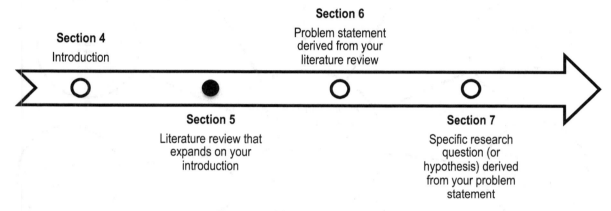

Section 4

Introduction

Section 6

Problem statement
derived from your
literature review

Section 5

Literature review that
expands on your
introduction

Section 7

Specific research
question (or
hypothesis) derived
from your problem
statement

Identifying the Problem

In general, your literature review directly follows and expands on your Introduction section (Section 4), as previously described. Besides increasing your knowledge base on your problem area, writing a literature review provides you with an opportunity to demonstrate your skills in two areas:

1. ***Information-seeking skills****:* the ability to identify a set of useful articles and books by scanning the relevant literature efficiently, using manual and computerized methods.

2. ***Critical appraisal skills****:* the ability to identify and critique previously published research studies.

Whereas your Introduction section told your readers where your proposal is headed, by describing what you want to do, how you are going to do it, and why your work is significant, Section 5 validates your efforts and substantiates the need to

study your problem area further. You will do this by citing other authoritative sources who are also knowledgeable about your problem area.

As you know, your literature review has to be professionally written; that is, it's not simply a list of monotonous, mind-numbing descriptions of one study after another. This is the kiss of death in a literature review. Never begin your paragraphs with the name of a researcher and a description of his or her research study. Instead, you have three choices on how to organize your literature: chronological, thematic, or methodological.

- ***Chronological.*** If your review follows the chronological method, you write about the research studies you have found according to when they were published.

- ***Thematic.*** Thematic reviews of the literature are simply organized around a topic or issue, rather than the progression of time. See Box 5.1 as an example.

- ***Methodological.*** A methodological approach focuses on the research methods that the researchers used to gather their data rather than on the content of the material. Thus, survey, observational, experimental, quantitative, and/or qualitative studies are grouped together. We do not recommend this method; rather, the thematic method illustrated in Box 5.1 is a better choice.

Pick one of the three methods—and only one. Talk with your instructor about which method you should use, given your research topic area.

		Tips for Writing a Literature Review	
#		**Tips**
46	**Yes No**	Check to see if you know how to do electronic and manual literature searches.
47	**Yes No**	Check to see if you know how to write literature reviews and have read the appropriate chapter(s) in your research methods text before you complete Section 5.

48	Yes No	Check to see if your literature review is written chronologically, thematically, or methodologically. Pick one theme and only one theme.
49	Yes No	Check to see that you discussed the assumptions you are going to make before you begin your proposed research study.
50	Yes No	Check to see that you have cited and discussed research studies that ran contrary to your perspective.
51	Yes No	Check to see that you have shown how your proposed study relates to the larger, ongoing dialogue in the literature about your research area, filling in gaps and extending prior studies.
52	Yes No	Check to see that you have critically analyzed the literature; that is, instead of just listing and summarizing study after study, did you assess them by discussing their strengths and weaknesses?
53	Yes No	Check to see that you discussed the historical development of your research problem (or issue) over time.
54	Yes No	Check to see that your literature review cited introductory texts, standard articles, chapters in books, grey material, online sources, and topical encyclopedias in an effort to sketch a solid orientation of the kinds of academic discussions in your problem area.
55	Yes No	Check to see that you have been judicious in your choice of exemplars—the literature you select should be directly pertinent and relevant to your study.

56	**Yes** ☺ **No** ☹	Check to see that you have avoided statements that imply that little has been done in your problem area or that what has been done is too extensive to permit an easy summary. Statements of this sort are usually taken as indications that you are not really familiar with the published literature.
57	**Yes** ☺ **No** ☹	Check to see that you cited previous projects and studies that are similar to what you are proposing.
58	**Yes** ☺ **No** ☹	Check to see that you discussed the research methods and data analyses that previous researchers have used when exploring your problem area.
59	**Yes** ☺ **No** ☹	Check to see that you have discussed all the key methodological issues that have arisen in your problem area: for example, problems in research designs (Section 8a), sampling (Section 8b), instrumentation (Section 8c), data collection methods (Section 8d), and data analyses (Section 8e). You don't want to make the same mistakes in your study.
60	**Yes** ☺ **No** ☹	Check to see that you have avoided the methodological and data analyses mistakes and/or errors that have been previously made by others.
61	**Yes** ☺ **No** ☹	Check to see that you have provided adequate conceptual and operational definitions of key terms (if appropriate).

62	Yes No	Check to see that you have clearly outlined exactly what you are going to be investigating as the particular focus of your proposed research project. For example, is there a gap in the previous literature? In relation to current knowledge (as reflected in the literature), what exactly do you intend to do? What theoretical model relates to your research topic?
63	Yes No	Check to see if you demonstrated how your project would extend the work that has been previously done.
64	Yes No	Check to see that your literature review discussed the most recent research findings in your area of study.
65	Yes No	Check to see if your literature review discussed the pressing problem that you want to address.
66	Yes No	Check to see that your literature review listed new research questions that could be derived from previous research findings.
67	Yes No	Check to see if you included a well-documented statement of the need/problem that is the basis for your project: that is, did you establish the need for your proposed research study?
68	Yes No	Check to see that you clearly outlined the theoretical model (if any) that you are going to use in your research topic.
69	Yes No	Check to see if you made your key points clearly and succinctly.

70	Yes No	Check to see if you have selected and referenced only the more appropriate citations.
71	Yes No	Check to see that you have been very careful in your use of language. It can be helpful to have a friend who is outside of your area of focus/expertise read your proposal to make sure that your language is readable and minimizes the use of jargon, trendy or "in" words, abbreviations, colloquial expressions, redundant phrases, and confusing language.
72	Yes No	Check to see that your literature search was wide enough to ensure that you have found all the relevant material. And has your search been narrow enough to exclude irrelevant material? Is the number of sources you have provided appropriate for the scope of your research project?
73	Yes No	Check to see if your overall literature review is brief, to the point, selective, and critical.
74	Yes No	Check to see if the citations you used are in APA style.
75	Yes No	Check to see that your readers will find your literature review relevant, appropriate, and useful.

76	Yes No	Check to see that you have NOT made one of the following eight major sins in your literature review: 1. Lacks organization and structure 2. Lacks focus, unity, and coherence 3. Is repetitive and verbose 4. Fails to cite influential papers 5. Fails to keep up with recent developments 6. Fails to critically evaluate cited papers 7. Cites irrelevant or trivial references 8. Depends too much on secondary sources
77	Yes No	Check to see that your literature review ends by delineating the "jumping-off place" for your proposed study. This will automatically lead to the next section of your proposal—the purpose of your study (Section 6).
78	Yes No	Check to see that your literature review did not go over the double-spaced, five- to seven-page limit. This page limit excludes the references that will go in your References section (Section 11).
79	Yes No	Check with your research instructor to see if he/she has any examples of literature reviews from other research proposals to show you.

Box 5.1 provides an example of a literature review from an article that appeared in a professional social work journal. The content of a published literature review in an article is identical to one written for a research proposal. Simply remember that just about everything you write for the Literature Review section within your research proposal will be recycled in the manuscript you finally submit for possible publication.

BOX 5.1

Example of a Literature Review Section from an Article That Appeared in a Professional Publication

Readiness for College Engagement among Students Who Have Aged Out of Foster Care[1]

LITERATURE REVIEW

Foster Youths' Barriers to Higher Education

One barrier to entering higher education for foster youth is their difficulty in completing primary and secondary education. Teenagers in foster care are involved in special-education classes at comparatively higher rates during their secondary educational experiences than non-foster-care teens (Courtney, Terao, & Bost, 2004; Pecora et al., 2006). Furthermore, they are more likely than their non-foster-care counterparts to drop out of high school, repeat a grade, or be suspended or expelled (Courtney, Terao, & Bost, 2004; Blome, 1997). When compared to non-foster youth, foster youth also have higher rates of changing schools that are related to their lower academic achievement and attainment (Blome, 1997; Pecora et al., 2006).

Foster youth also encounter general obstacles during their emerging years of young adulthood (i.e., 18–25 years of age). Youth aging out of foster care struggle more than other young adults across a number of important lifespan-developmental domains including: academics and education; finances and employment; housing; physical and mental health; social relationships and community connections; personal and cultural identity development; and life skills (Casey Family Programs, 2006). Many foster youth enter young adulthood with significant educational deficits, and the lasting effects of these deficits are evident in their dismal educational attainment (Courtney & Dworsky, 2006). The problems encountered by foster youth in each of the domains can be barriers to education.

The struggles that foster youth have with practical or systemic barriers in other life domains make it difficult to access or stay in school after aging out of foster care. For example, it is estimated that only about one-third of youth aging out of foster care left the system with basic resources such as a driver's license, cash, or basic necessities such as dishes (Pecora et al., 2006). Most do not have anyone to co-sign a loan or lease, which makes it difficult to secure safe housing.

Medicaid and funds for start-up goods are available in some states until age 21, but foster youth must be able to navigate the large and complicated state bureaucratic programs to receive these benefits. Courtney and colleagues (2010) found that the main barriers for higher-education access among foster youth were a lack of financial resources, the need to be in full-time employment, parenting responsibilities, and a lack of transportation. These practical and systemic obstacles provide some understanding as to why foster youth are less likely to access and succeed in college.

Nonetheless, several studies have reported that a significant number of foster youth want to pursue a college degree. Courtney and colleagues (2010), for example, reported that 79 percent of the foster youth in their study wanted to go to college. McMillen, Auslander, Elze, White, and Thompson (2003) reported similar findings whereby 70 percent of the foster youth they surveyed planned to attend college.

Foster Youth Attending College

A recent study that controlled for race and gender found that foster youth attending a four-year university were more likely to drop out of college compared to low-income first-generation students who had not lived in foster care (Day, Dworsky, Fogarty, & Damashek, 2011). However, there is a paucity of research exploring the reasons foster youth are less likely to succeed in college. We found three studies that investigate how foster youth fare in college settings.

Merdinger, Hines, Osterling, and Wyatt (2005) surveyed an ethnically diverse sample of 216 college students who spent an average of seven to eight years, and three placements, in foster care. They found that only about one quarter of these students felt prepared to live independently upon exiting the foster-care system, and about the same percentage believed that the foster-care system had sufficiently prepared them for college.

The majority of the sample was succeeding academically, but reported challenges with finances, psychological distress, and access to health care. Social support from friends and family was identified as a factor that possibly contributed to the educational success of the sample.

Davis (2006) reviewed the many factors that inhibit the ability of foster youth to develop the strong academic foundation necessary to be successful in higher education. These factors included challenges encountered during primary and secondary education, multiple school changes, incidence of disruptive behaviors in the classroom, and higher incidence of learning delays.

Foster youth also had far less personal income than their peers but were awarded a sufficient level of financial aid so that it did not impact their choice of institution. Davis noted that although state and federal programs aim to provide financial support to former foster youth enrolled in postsecondary education, such support is inadequate when not accompanied by structured social and academic support efforts.

Dworsky and Perez (2010) collected information from a nonrandom sample of 98 college students who participated in a campus support program for former foster youth in Washington or California. The sample was racially diverse, primarily female, and had an average age of 20 years old. Nearly all participants placed value on academic guidance such as advice on choosing courses or declaring a major, and many also asserted the importance of mentoring and leadership opportunities.

Students overall reported that their campus support-program participation provided them with a sense of belonging in a way similar to that which one might feel in a family setting. Though students also found financial aid and housing assistance to be of great importance, Dworsky and Perez (2010) noted that students were more likely to report gaining a sense of family through the program than they were to report receiving material assistance.

With the assistance of federal and state funding, foster youth are finding their way to higher-education institutions in increasing numbers (Fried, 2008). Colleges are starting to take notice of these young adults as evidenced by the growing number of campus programs designed to provide financial, academic, and other supports to students who have aged out of the foster care system (Casey Family Programs, 2010a; Dworsky & Perez, 2010), yet little is known about foster youths' level of readiness to engage in college.

Even less is known about foster youths' personal, social, interpersonal, academic, and career-development needs during their transition into college and ways that child welfare and higher education professionals can offer assistance.

REFERENCES

Arnett, J.J. (2000). Emerging adulthood: A theory of development from the late teens through the twenties. *American Psychologist, 55,* 469–480.

Avery, R.J., & Freundlich, M. (2009). You're all grown up now: Termination of foster care support at age 18. *Journal of Adolescence, 32,* 247–257.

Blome, W.W. (1997). What happens to foster kids: Educational experiences of a random sample of foster youth and a matched group of non-foster youth. *Child and Adolescent Social Work Journal, 14,* 41–53.

Casey Family Programs (2006). *It's my life: Postsecondary education and training and financial aid excerpt.* Seattle, WA: Author. Retrieved on June 7, 2011 from: www.casey.org/Resources/Publications/IMLPostsecondaryEd.htm

Casey Family Programs (2009). *Providing effective financial aid assistance to students from foster care and unaccompanied homeless youth.* Seattle, WA. Retrieved on June 7, 2011 from: http://www.casey.org/Resources/Publications/ProvidingEffectiveFinancialAid.htm.

Casey Family Programs (2010a). *Supporting success: Improving higher education outcomes for students from foster care* (Version 2.0). Seattle, WA: Author. Retrieved on June 7, 2011 from: http://www.casey.org/Resources/Publications/SupportingSuccess.htm.

Casey Family Programs (2010b). *Improving higher education outcomes for young adults from foster care selected readings and resources.* Seattle, WA: Author.

Child Welfare Information Gateway. (2011). *Foster care statistics 2009.* Washington, DC: U.S. Department of Health and Human Services, Children's Bureau. Retrieved on June 7, 2011 from: http://www.childwelfare.gov/pubs/factsheets/foster.cfm

Cook, A., Blaustein, M., Spinazzola, & van der Kolk, B. (2003). *Complex trauma in children and adolescents.* White paper from the National Child Traumatic Stress Network. Retrieved on June 7, 2011 from: www.NCTSNet.org.

Courtney, M.E., & Dworksy, A. (2006). Early outcomes for young adults transitioning from out-of-home care in the USA. *Child and Family Social Work, 11*, 209–219.

Courtney, M.E., Dworsky, A., Lee, J., & Raap, M. (2010). *Midwest evaluation of the adult functioning of former foster youth: Outcomes at ages 23 and 24.* Chicago: Chapin Hall Center for Children at the University of Chicago.

Courtney, M.E., Terao, S., & Bost, N. (2004). *Midwest evaluation of the adult functioning of former foster youth: Conditions of the youth preparing to leave state care.* Chicago: Chapin Hall Center for Children at the University of Chicago.

Cueso, J. (2005). Decided, undecided, and in transition: Implications for academic advisement, career counseling, and student retention. In R.S. Feldman (Ed.), *Improving the first year of college: Research and practice* (pp. 27–48). Mahwah, NJ: Erlbaum.

Davis, R.J. (2006). *College access, financial aid and college success for undergraduates from foster care.* Washington, DC: National Association of Student Financial Aid Administrators.

Day, A. (2009). Coming full circle: From child victim to childcare professional. In W.K. Brown and J.R. Seita, *Growing up in the care of strangers.* Tallahassee, FL: William Gladden Foundation Press.

Day, A., Dworsky, A., Fogarty, K., & Damashek, A. (2011). An examination of post-secondary retention and graduation among foster care youth enrolled in a four-year university, *Children and Youth Services Review*, doi:10.1016/j.childyouth.2011.08.004.

Dworsky, A., & Courtney, M. (2009). Addressing the mental health service needs of foster youth during the transition to adulthood: How big is the problem and what can states do? *Journal of Adolescent Health, 44*, 1–2.

Dworsky, A., & Perez, A. (2010). Helping former foster youth graduate from college through campus support programs. *Children and Youth Services Review, 32*, 255–263.

Fried, T. (2008). Community colleges step up to support foster care students. *Community College Journal* (February/March), 38–39.

Geenan, S., & Powers, L.E. (2007). Tomorrow is another problem: The experiences of youth in foster care during their transition into adulthood. *Children and Youth Services Review, 29,* 1085–1101.

Hines, A.M., Merdinger, J., & Wyatt, P. (2005). Former foster youth attending college: Resilience and the transition to young adulthood. *American Journal of Orthopsychiatry, 75*, 381–394.

Iglehart, A.P. (1995). Readiness for independence: Comparison of foster care, kinship care, and non-foster care adolescents. *Children and Youth Services Review, 17*, 417–432.

Jackson, S., & Martin, P.Y. (1998). Surviving the care system: Education and resilience. *Journal of Adolescence, 21*, 569–583.

Jehangir, R.R. (2010). *Higher education and first-generation students: Cultivating community, voice, and place for the new majority.* Basingstoke: Palgrave Macmillan.

Kools, S. (1997). Adolescent identity development in foster care. *Family Relations, 46*, 263–271.

Kools, S. (1999). Self-protection in adolescents in foster care. *Journal of Child and Adolescent Psychiatric Nursing, 12*, 139–152.

McMillen, J.C., Auslander, W., Elze, D., White, T., & Thompson, R. (2003). Educational experiences and aspirations of older youth in foster care. *Child Welfare, 82*, 475–495.

McMillen, J.C., & Raghavan, R. (2009). Pediatric to adult mental health service use of young people leaving the foster care system. *Journal of Adolescent Health, 44*, 7–13.

McMillen, J.C., & Tucker, J. (1999). The status of older adolescents at exit from out-of home care, *Child Welfare, 78*, 339–360.

McMillen, J.C., Vaughn, M.G., & Shook, J.J. (2008). Aging out of foster care and legal involvement: Toward a typology of risk. *Social Service Review, 82*, 419–446.

Merdinger, J.M., Hines, A.M., Osterling, K.L., & Wyatt, P. (2005). Pathways to college for former foster youth: Understanding factors that contribute to educational success. *Child Welfare, 84*, 867–896.

Park, J.M., Metraux, S., & Culhane, D.P. (2005). Childhood out-of-home placement and dynamics of public shelter utilization among young homeless adults. *Children and Youth Services Review, 27*, 533–546.

Pecora, P.J., Williams, J., Kessler, R.C., Hiripi, E., O'Brien, K., Emerson, J., Herrick, M.A., & Torres, D. (2006). Assessing the educational achievements of adults who were formerly placed in family foster care. *Child & Family Social Work, 11*, 220–231.

Reilly, T. (2003). Transition from care: Status and outcomes of youth who age out of foster care. *Child Welfare, 82*, 727–746.

Samuels, G.M., & Price, J.M. (2008). What doesn't kill you makes you stronger: Survivalist self-reliance and risk among young adults aging out of foster care. *Children and Youth Services Review, 30*, 1198–1210.

Seita, J.R. (2001). Growing up without family privilege. *Reclaiming Children and Youth, 10*, 130–132.

Sheehy, A., Oldham, E., Zanghi, M., Ansell, D., Correia, P., & Copeland, R. (2000). *Promising practices: Supporting the transition of youth served by the foster care system.* Baltimore: Annie E. Casey Foundation.

Stratil, M.L. (2001). *College Student Inventory Manual.* Iowa City, IA: Noel-Levitz, Inc.

Stratil, M.L. (2009). *College Student Inventory™: Form A.* Coralville, IA: Noel-Levitz, Inc.

Unrau, Y.A., & Grinnell, R.M., Jr. (2005). The impact of social work research courses on research self-efficacy for social work students. *Social Work Education, 24*, 639–651.

Unrau, Y.A., Seita, J.R., & Putney, K.S. (2008). Former foster youth remember multiple placement moves: A journey of loss and hope. *Children and Youth Services Review, 30*, 1256–1266.

van der Kolk, B.A. (2005). Developmental trauma disorder: Toward a rational diagnosis for children with complex trauma histories. *Psychiatric Annals, 35*, 401–408.

Wolanin, T.R. (2005*). Higher education opportunities for foster youth: A primer for policymakers.* Washington, DC: Institute for Higher Education Policy.

---

[1]Unrau, Y.A., Font, S.A., & Rawls, G. (2012). Readiness for college engagement among students who have aged out of foster care. *Children and Youth Services Review, 34*, 76–83.

 Homework Assignment 5.1

Writing Literature Review Sections for Research Proposals

Box 5.1 presents the Literature Review section from a social work journal article. Download and read the article. Now that you are familiar with the research study depicted in Box 5.1:

In the white space below, write the Literature Review section you feel the authors *should have* written for the research proposal their study was based upon. The box will expand as you type.

NOTE: You do not have a copy of the authors' research proposal. You only have a copy of the article that resulted from the implementation of their proposal. Your main objective is to edit, revise, rearrange, and/or modify the authors' published Literature Review section as you think it *should have* appeared in their research proposal.

- Use all the tips in this section to write your hypothetical proposal's Literature Review section (e.g., clear and succinct key points).

- Submit your revised Literature Review section to your instructor, pointing out all the revisions you made and why you made them.

Your Name(s):
Your Identification Number(s) (if any):
Assignment 5.1

Type your revised Literature Review section here.
(Box will automatically expand as you type)

Section 5
Writing a Literature Review Section for Your Research Proposal

Write the Literature Review section for your research proposal in the white space provided below. The box will expand as you type.

- Use all the tips in this section to write your literature review (e.g., clear and succinct key points).
- If possible, show your proposal's Title, Abstract, Introduction, and Literature Review sections to your classmates for their feedback.
- Revise all four sections based on your classmates' feedback.
- Submit all four sections to your instructor for comment.

Your Name(s):

Your Identification Number(s) (if any):

Title of Your Research Proposal:

Type your Abstract, Introduction, and Literature Review sections here.

(Box will automatically expand as you type)

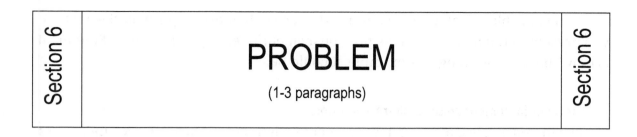

PROBLEM

(1-3 paragraphs)

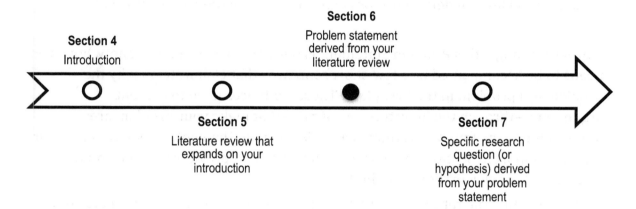

Section 4

Introduction

Section 6

Problem statement derived from your literature review

Section 5

Literature review that expands on your introduction

Section 7

Specific research question (or hypothesis) derived from your problem statement

Identifying the Problem

Section 6 of your research proposal is devoted to the problem area you wish to study, commonly referred to as a Problem Statement. It must be straightforwardly derived from your Literature Review section. Your research problem needs to be a one-sentence statement that provides a clear and concise description of a general "issue" that currently exists. And you want to study this issue further.

Your problem area must stand out. Your readers must easily recognize it as it provides the overall context for your proposed study and establishes the foundation for everything that will follow in your research proposal.

Furthermore, if the problem area you wish to study will involve the cooperation with a social work agency that sees a need for your study, your proposal should include a support letter from the agency's executive director. A copy of the letter is placed in an appendix (e.g., Appendix A in this book), but it should be referred to in this section.

A good Problem Statement generates the research question (or hypothesis) that you present in the next section. As previously mentioned, a good Problem Statement is only one sentence long. For example, it could be:

Problem Statement (without literary support)
The increasing use of micro-management techniques by social work supervisors is creating fear, anxiety, and a loss of productivity in their supervisees.

Yup, sure enough, this Problem Statement is one sentence in length. It now, however, needs to be accompanied by a few short sentences that elaborate on why the problem is a problem in the first place. These sentences need to present arguments—through the literature, of course—that make your problem area important enough for you to study further. More often than not, the sources for your literary support in Section 6 will have been mentioned previously when you were discussing the relevant literature in the last section.

While noting the rationale for your proposed project's boundaries and for the specified choice of your focus to the exclusion of others, you need to allude to the next section of your research proposal, the Research Question (Section 7), and to the research methodology you will use to answer your question (Section 8).

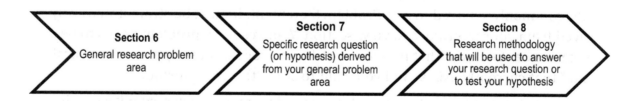

If appropriate, your Problem Statement should be presented within a context, and that context should be provided and briefly explained. That is, you should discuss the *conceptual or theoretical framework* in which your proposed study is embedded. Clearly and succinctly identify and explain the *theoretical framework* that underlies your proposed study and explain how you identified your "problem" as a problem. You should state your problem in terms intelligible to someone who is generally sophisticated but relatively uninformed in the problem area of your proposed study.

Box 6.1 provides an example of how a Problem Statement was formulated within a theoretical framework.

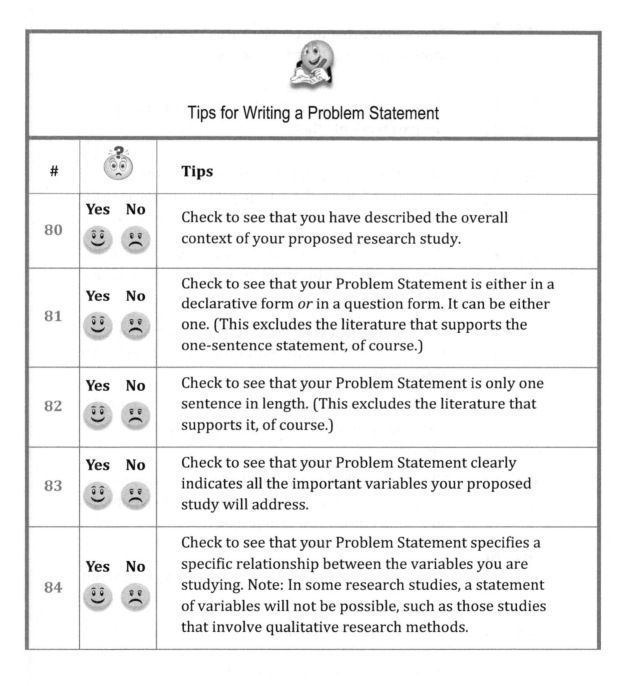

Tips for Writing a Problem Statement

#	Yes / No	Tips
80	Yes No	Check to see that you have described the overall context of your proposed research study.
81	Yes No	Check to see that your Problem Statement is either in a declarative form *or* in a question form. It can be either one. (This excludes the literature that supports the one-sentence statement, of course.)
82	Yes No	Check to see that your Problem Statement is only one sentence in length. (This excludes the literature that supports it, of course.)
83	Yes No	Check to see that your Problem Statement clearly indicates all the important variables your proposed study will address.
84	Yes No	Check to see that your Problem Statement specifies a specific relationship between the variables you are studying. Note: In some research studies, a statement of variables will not be possible, such as those studies that involve qualitative research methods.

85	Yes No	Check to see that you have provided a rationale for your Problem Statement.
86	Yes No	Check to see that the problem area you propose to study is of current interest (or topical).
87	Yes No	Check to see that your Problem Statement builds upon the past work of others.
88	Yes No	Check to see that you have indicated how the population (research participants) you propose to use in your study is important, influential, or popular.
89	Yes No	Check to see that you have indicated that the problem area you wish to study will in all likelihood continue into the future.
90	Yes No	Check to see that your Problem Statement is not obscure, poorly formulated, or masked in an extended discussion.
91	Yes No	Check to see that your Problem Statement is actually solvable given your time frame, resources, and commitment.
92	Yes No	Check to see that you are *not* trying to answer too many research problems or test too many hypotheses in your proposed research project.
93	Yes No	Check to see that your problem area really stands out.
94	Yes No	Check to see that you have provided a discussion of the conceptual and/or theoretical framework in which your problem area is embedded.

95	Yes No	Check to see that your Problem Statement contains only variables that are measurable. (More will be said about this in Section 8c on Instrumentation.)
96	Yes No	Check to see that you have stated your problem in terms that are intelligible to someone who is generally sophisticated but relatively uninformed in the problem area of your proposed study.
97	Yes No	Check to see that you have been judicious in your choice of exemplars—the literature you select must be directly pertinent and relevant to your problem area.
98	Yes No	Check to see that your proposed study is replicable. The significance of your proposed project depends, in part, on its ability to be duplicated.
99	Yes No	Check to see that you have identified the general analysis approach you propose to take. This more often than not is implicit in the statement.
100	Yes No	Check to see that your Problem Statement did not go over the maximum three-paragraph limit. (This includes the supporting literature.)
101	Yes No	Check with your research instructor to see if he/she has any examples of Problem Statements from other research proposals to show you.

BOX 6.1

Example of a Theoretical Framework and Problem Statement
from an Article That Appeared in a Professional Journal

**Exploring Out-Of-Home Placement as a Moderator of
Help-Seeking Behavior among Adolescents Who Are High Risk[1]**

COMPONENTS OF HELP-SEEKING BEHAVIORS

The first component of help-seeking behaviors is predisposing factors. The model suggests that service users possess a variety of predisposing factors that determine whether individuals seek out help for themselves. These include demographics (e.g., gender, race, age), social structure (e.g., education, occupation, social networks, culture), and health care beliefs (e.g., attitudes about health and health services).

The second component covers enabling factors, which are factors assumed to directly facilitate an individual's help-seeking behaviors. Availability and accessibility to services (e.g., health insurance and transportation), general know-how to gain use of services, and social relationships that assist with service use are included as enabling factors in Andersen's model.

The third component is known as the level of need factor, which is the severity of a problem suffered by the individual. It influences the likelihood of seeking help for oneself. Self-perceived need and professionally evaluated need are distinguished in the model

In sum, Andersen (1995) argued that all three factors—predisposing, enabling, and level of need—influence whether individuals set out to seek help for their problems. It should be noted that the current study does not test Andersen's model. Rather, his model is used as an organizing framework to examine the role that out-of home placement plays in the help-seeking behaviors among a group of adolescents who are high risk in relation to their physical and mental health problems.

Andersen's model provides a simple structure for describing complex relationships. Furthermore, others have applied it to foster care as a framework to critique health care utilization in the foster care system (Combs-Orme et al., 1991) and to investigate predictors of health service use by foster parents for children with psychiatric diagnoses (Zima, Bussing, Yang, & Belin, 2000).

There is a growing body of literature that investigates the factors predicting help-seeking behaviors between child and adolescent populations. This study's review of the literature was restricted to research studies that were conducted on

North American samples that included youth between ages 13 and 19 years.

Previous research studies investigating help-seeking behaviors and service utilization were reviewed, **as the current study's aim is to understand which factors predict help-seeking behaviors in adolescent populations.**

REFERENCES

Andersen, R.M. (1995). Revisiting the behavioral model and access to medical care: Does it matter? *Journal of Health and Social Behavior, 36*, 1–10.

Combs-Orme, T., Chernoff, V., & Karger, R. (1991). Utilization of health care by foster children: Application of a theoretical model. *Children and Youth Services Review, 11*, 113–129.

Zima, B.T., Bussing, R., Yang, X., & Belin, T.R. (2000). Help-seeking steps and service use for children in foster care. *Journal of Behavioral Health Services & Research, 27*, 271–285.

---

[1]Unrau, Y.A., & Grinnell, R.M., Jr. (2005). Exploring out-of-home placement as a moderator of help-seeking behavior among adolescents who are high risk. *Research on Social Work Practice, 15,* 516–530.

Homework Assignment 6.1

Writing Problem Sections for Research Proposals

Box 6.1 presents the Problem section from a social work journal article. Download and read the article. Now that you are familiar with the research study depicted in Box 6.1:

In the white space below, write the Problem section you feel the authors *should have* written for the research proposal their study was based upon. The box will expand as you type.

NOTE: You do not have a copy of the authors' research proposal. You only have a copy of the article that resulted from the implementation of their proposal. Your main objective is to edit, revise, rearrange, and/or modify the authors' published Problem section as you think it *should have* appeared in their research proposal.

- Use all the tips in this section to write your hypothetical proposal's Problem section (e.g., builds upon past work of others).

- Submit your revised Problem section to your instructor, pointing out all the revisions you made and why you made them.

Your Name(s):
Your Identification Number(s) (if any):
Assignment 6.1

Type your revised Problem section here.
(Box will automatically expand as you type)

Section 6
Writing a Problem Section for Your Research Proposal

Write a Problem section for your research proposal in the white space provided below. The box will expand as you type.

- Use all the tips in this section to write your Problem section (e.g., builds on past work of others).
- If possible, show your Problem section to your classmates for their feedback.
- Revise your Problem section based on your classmates' feedback.
- Submit your Problem section to your instructor for comments.

Your Name(s):

Your Identification Number(s) (if any):

Title of Your Research Proposal:

Type your Problem section here.
(Box will automatically expand as you type)

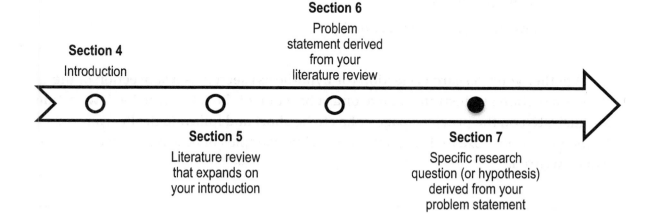

Section 4

Introduction

Section 6

Problem
statement derived
from your
literature review

Section 5

Literature review
that expands on
your introduction

Section 7

Specific research
question (or hypothesis)
derived from your
problem statement

Identifying the Problem

Section 7 is short—very short. But just because it's short doesn't mean it's not important. It must follow logically from your Problem, which was logically derived from your Literature Review.

Section 7 simply provides the specific research question your study is going to answer, or the hypothesis you are going to test. If your research question (or hypothesis) is not extraordinarily clear to you, it won't be clear to those who read your proposal.

Many times, the Research Question (or hypothesis) section is a subsection of the Literature Review section, as illustrated below. In this instance, there would not be a separate Section 7 within the research proposal since it was incorporated into Section 5. And sometimes the Problem section is imbedded within the Literature Review section as well. So your outline could look like:

LITERATURE REVIEW (Section 5)

Problem (Section 6)

Research Question (Section 7)

Or,

LITERATURE REVIEW (Section 5)

Problem (Section 6)

Research Question (Section 7)

Whether your Research Question (or hypothesis) section is a subsection of the Problem section as illustrated above or a subsection of the Literature Review section as illustrated on the previous page, it has to be short and follow logically from your Problem section. Boxes 7.1 through 7.3 provide examples of how research questions can be written.

Tips for Writing a Research Question (or Hypothesis)		
#		**Tips**
102	**Yes No**	Check to see that your research question to be answered (or your hypothesis to be tested) is logically linked to your Problem section; that is, this section must logically flow out of your Problem section.
103	**Yes No**	Check to see that your research question starts with a sentence that begins "The purpose of this study is . . ." This will clarify your own mind as to your study's purpose, and it will directly and explicitly inform your readers about what exactly you propose to do.

104	**Yes** ☺ **No** ☹	Check to see that your research question to be answered (or your hypothesis to be tested) is an ethical one.
105	**Yes** ☺ **No** ☹	Check to see that you are prepared to interpret any possible outcomes with respect to your research question or hypothesis.
106	**Yes** ☺ **No** ☹	Check to see if you have visualized in your mind's eye the tables and other summary devices you will use that will eventually contain your study's results.
107	**Yes** ☺ **No** ☹	Check to see if you made a clear and careful distinction between your dependent and independent variables, and be certain they are clear to your readers. (Not all research studies contain independent and dependent variables.)
108	**Yes** ☺ **No** ☹	Check to be sure you were excruciatingly consistent in your use of terms. If appropriate, use the same pattern of wording (and word order) in all your research questions (or hypotheses).
109	**Yes** ☺ **No** ☹	Check to see if you have access to the data that are needed to answer your research question (or test your hypothesis).
110	**Yes** ☺ **No** ☹	Check to see that you did not go over the two-paragraph limit.
111	**Yes** ☺ **No** ☹	Check to see that you have all the necessary skills (or can develop them) to find an answer to your research question (or to test your hypothesis).
112	**Yes** ☺ **No** ☹	Check with your research instructor to see if he/she has any examples of research problems (or hypotheses) from other research proposals to show you.

BOX 7.1

Example of Research Questions from an Article
That Appeared in a Professional Journal

Voucher Users and Revitalized Public-Housing Residents 6 Years after Displacement[1]

RESEARCH QUESTIONS

1. How did participants experience the application process of moving back to College Town?
2. How many residents moved back to College Town, and what reasons did they give for returning?
3. What reasons did residents give for not applying to move back to College Town?
4. How satisfied were residents who returned to College Town?
5. How did public-housing residents compare with voucher users on standardized measures of material hardship?
6. A total of 6 years after displacement, how did public-housing residents compare with voucher users for overall economic well-being?

---

[1]Brooks, F., Lewinson, T., Aszman, J., & Wolk, J. (2012). Voucher users and revitalized public-housing residents 6 years after displacement. *Research on Social Work Practice, 22,* 10–19.

BOX 7.2

Example of Research Questions from an Article
That Appeared in a Professional Journal

Evaluating Predictors of Program Attrition among Women Mandated into Batterer Intervention Treatment[1]

RESEARCH QUESTIONS

The current study addresses the following research questions:

1. What exactly are the differences in demographic and psychosocial variables between program completers versus program dropouts for women batterers, and what do these differences mean in terms of program planning and implementation?

2. Do referral source and level of supervision affect rates of program completion among women batterers, and if so, what are the implications for the criminal justice system?

---

[1]Buttell, F., Powers, D., & Wong, A. (2012). Evaluating predictors of program attrition among women mandated into batterer intervention treatment. *Research on Social Work Practice, 22,* 20–28.

BOX 7.3

Example of Research Questions (Purpose) from an Article
That Appeared in a Professional Journal

Readiness for College Engagement among Students Who Have Aged Out of Foster Care[1]

The purpose of this study, therefore, is twofold:

1. to identify and measure foster youths' readiness for college engagement, (i.e., academic motivation, social motivation, receptivity to student services, general coping).
2. to compare the readiness for college engagement among freshman foster youth prior to the start of college with the readiness for college engagement among freshman in general.
3. In addition, this article describes the first-semester performance of freshman foster youth compared with other freshman enrolled in the same university.

[1]Unrau, Y.A., Font, S.A., & Rawls, G. (2012). Readiness for college engagement among students who have aged out of foster care. *Children and Youth Services Review, 34*, 76–83.

Homework Assignment 7.1

Writing Research Question (or Hypothesis) Sections for Research Proposals

Boxes 7.1 to 7.3 present three Research Question sections from three different social work journal articles. Download and read one of the articles. Now that you are familiar with the research study depicted in the article you selected:

In the white space below, write a Research Question section you feel the authors *should have* written for the research proposal their study was based upon. The box will expand as you type.

NOTE: You do not have a copy of the authors' research proposal. You only have a copy of the article that resulted from the implementation of their proposal. Your main objective is to edit, revise, rearrange, and/or modify the authors' published Research Question section as you think it *should have* appeared in their research proposal.

* Use all the tips in this section to write your hypothetical proposal's Research Question section (e.g., is it ethical?).

* Submit your revised Research Question section to your instructor, pointing out all the revisions you made and why you made them.

Your Name(s):
Your Identification Number(s) (if any):
Assignment 7.1. Title of Selected Article:

Type your revised Research Question (or Hypothesis) section here.
(Box will automatically expand as you type)

Section 7
Writing a Research Question (or Hypothesis)
Section for Your Research Proposal

Write a Research Question (or hypothesis) section for your research proposal in the white space provided below. The box will expand as you type.

- Use all the tips in this section to write your Research Question (or hypothesis) section (e.g., is it ethical?).
- If possible, show your Research Question (or hypothesis) section to your classmates for their feedback.
- Revise your Research Question (or hypothesis) section based on your classmates' feedback.
- Submit your Research Question (or hypothesis) section to your instructor for comments.

Your Name(s):

Your Identification Number(s) (if any):

Title of Your Research Proposal:

Type your Research Question (or Hypothesis) section here.
(Box will automatically expand as you type)

PART IV
Solving the Problem

Once you have specified the research question you want to solve (or the hypothesis you want to test) in Section 7, you now have to state how you are going to solve your research question (or test your hypothesis) in Section 8.

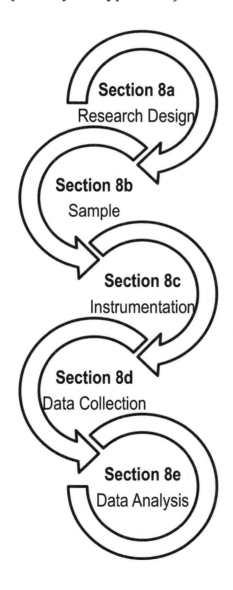

Section 8a
Research Design

Section 8b
Sample

Section 8c
Instrumentation

Section 8d
Data Collection

Section 8e
Data Analysis

METHOD

(3–5 pages)

In the last section you formulated a research question (or hypothesis) for your proposed study. You will now need to describe how you propose to answer your research question (or to test your hypothesis)—the main purpose of Section 8. The Method section contains five highly interrelated subsections:

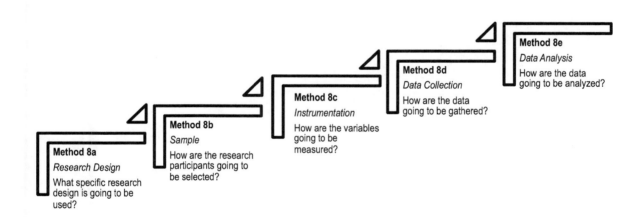

Method 8a

Research Design

What specific research design is going to be used?

Method 8b

Sample

How are the research participants going to be selected?

Method 8c

Instrumentation

How are the variables going to be measured?

Method 8d

Data Collection

How are the data going to be gathered?

Method 8e

Data Analysis

How are the data going to be analyzed?

RESEARCH DESIGN

(1–2 paragraphs)

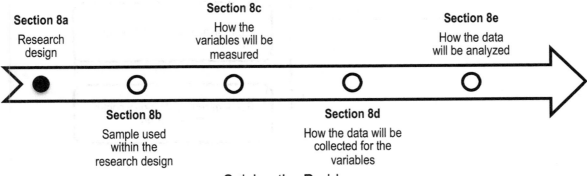

Section 8a

Research design

Section 8c

How the variables will be measured

Section 8e

How the data will be analyzed

Section 8b

Sample used within the research design

Section 8d

How the data will be collected for the variables

Solving the Problem

There are many ways to classify research designs. We are going to classify them into those that use only one group of research participants (known as one-group research designs) and those that use two or more groups of research participants (known as two-group designs) as illustrated:

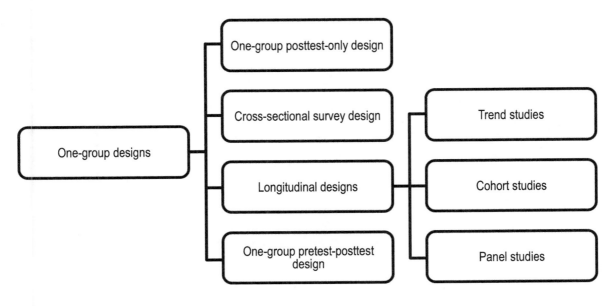

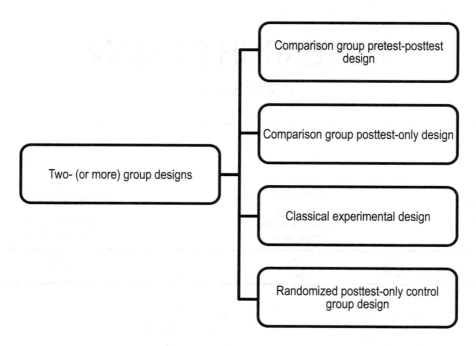

You need to justify the research design you propose to use that is supposed to answer your research question (or to test your hypothesis). You then need to present a brief synopsis of your overall research design—quantitative, qualitative, or mixed (both quantitative *and* qualitative).

Tips for Writing a Research Design Section

#		Tips
113	Yes No	Before you select a research design, check to see that you genuinely understand what each research design is used for and you know the advantages and disadvantages of each one. You must read the chapter(s) in your research methods text before you complete this section of your research proposal.
114	Yes No	Before you select a research design, check to see that you have considered the pros and cons of alternative designs, paying particular attention to how you are going to control extraneous variables that may produce bias and confounding results.
115	Yes No	Check to see that you have made it extraordinary clear which specific research design you propose to use. State your selected design in words such as "This study will use a one-group posttest-only design."
116	Yes No	Check to see that you have made a clear connection between the research question (or hypothesis) you formulated in Section 7 and the research design you are going to use to answer that question (or test your hypothesis), Section 8a.

117	**Yes No**	Check to see that you have stated what your independent and dependent variables are (if you have any). You do not have to inform the readers at this point of how you are going to measure the variables—that's described in Section 8c on Instrumentation. Remember, your study does not have to have an independent or dependent variable.
118	**Yes No**	Before you select a research design, check to see that you truly understand how the threats to internal and external validity factors affect each research design and especially the research design you have chosen to use in your proposed study.
119	**Yes No**	Check to see that you have clearly stated how the research design you have finally selected for your proposed research study controls for one of the threats to internal validity: **history** (if applicable, of course). If your research design doesn't control for **history**, you need to point out that this is one of the limitations of your study that will be discussed further in Section 9—the section where you pay attention to how the internal validity threat of **history** directly affects the interpretation of your study's findings.

120	**Yes No**	Check to see that you have clearly stated how the research design you have finally selected for your proposed research study controls for one of the threats to internal validity: **maturation** (if applicable, of course). If your research design doesn't control for **maturation**, you need to point out that this is one of the limitations of your study that will be discussed further in Section 9—the section where you pay attention to how the internal validity threat of **maturation** directly affects the interpretation of your study's findings.
121	**Yes No**	Check to see that you have clearly stated how the research design you have finally selected for your proposed research study controls for one of the threats to internal validity: **testing (or initial measurement effects)** (if applicable, of course). If your research design doesn't control for **testing**, you need to point out that this is one of the limitations of your study that will be discussed further in Section 9—the section where you pay attention to how the internal validity threat of **testing** directly affects the interpretation of your study's findings.

122	**Yes** **No** ☺ ☹	Check to see that you have clearly stated how the research design you have finally selected for your proposed research study controls for one of the threats to internal validity: **instrumentation error** (if applicable, of course). If your research design doesn't control for **instrumentation error**, you need to point out that this is one of the limitations of your study that will be discussed further in Section 9—the section where you pay attention to how the internal validity threat of **instrumentation error** directly affects the interpretation of your study's findings.
123	**Yes** **No** ☺ ☹	Check to see that you have clearly stated how the research design you have finally selected for your proposed research study controls for one of the threats to internal validity: **statistical regression** (if applicable, of course). If your research design doesn't control for **statistical regression**, you need to point out that this is one of the limitations of your study that will be discussed further in Section 9—the section where you pay attention to how the internal validity threat of **statistical regression error** directly affects the interpretation of your study's findings.

124	**Yes** **No**	Check to see that you have clearly stated how the research design you have finally selected for your proposed research study controls for one of the threats to internal validity: **differential selection of research participants** (if applicable, of course). If your research design doesn't control for **differential selection of research participants**, you need to point out that this is one of the limitations of your study that will be discussed further in Section 9—the section where you pay attention to how the internal validity threat of **differential selection of research participants** directly affects the interpretation of your study's findings.
125	**Yes** **No**	Check to see that you have clearly stated how the research design you have finally selected for your proposed research study controls for one of the threats to internal validity: **mortality** (if applicable, of course). If your research design doesn't control for **mortality**, you need to point out that this is one of the limitations of your study that will be discussed further in Section 9—the section where you pay attention to how the internal validity threat of **mortality** directly affects the interpretation of your study's findings.

126	**Yes** **No** 😊 😦	Check to see that you have clearly stated how the research design you have finally selected for your proposed research study controls for one of the threats to internal validity: **reactive effects of research participants** (if applicable, of course). If your research design doesn't control for **reactive effects of research participants**, you need to point out that this is one of the limitations of your study that will be discussed further in Section 9—the section where you pay attention to how the internal validity threat of **reactive effects of research participants** directly affects the interpretation of your study's findings.
127	**Yes** **No** 😊 😦	Check to see that you have clearly stated how the research design you have finally selected for your proposed research study controls for one of the threats to internal validity: **interaction effects** (if applicable, of course). If your research design doesn't control for **interaction effects**, you need to point out that this is one of the limitations of your study that will be discussed further in Section 9—the section where you pay attention to how the internal validity threat of **interaction effects** directly affects the interpretation of your study's findings.

128	**Yes No** 😊 ☹️	Check to see that you have clearly stated how the research design you have finally selected for your proposed research study controls for one of the threats to internal validity: **diffusion of treatments** (if applicable, of course). If your research design doesn't control for **diffusion of treatments**, you need to point out that this is one of the limitations of your study that will be discussed further in Section 9—the section where you pay attention to how the internal validity threat of **diffusion of treatments** directly affects the interpretation of your study's findings.
129	**Yes No** 😊 ☹️	Check to see that you have clearly stated how the research design you have finally selected for your proposed research study controls for one of the threats to internal validity: **compensatory equalization** (if applicable, of course). If your research design doesn't control for **compensatory equalization**, you need to point out that this is one of the limitations of your study that will be discussed further in Section 9—the section where you pay attention to how the internal validity threat of **compensatory equalization** directly affects the interpretation of your study's findings.

130	**Yes No** 🙂 🙁	Check to see that you have clearly stated how the research design you have finally selected for your proposed research study controls for one of the threats to internal validity: **compensatory rivalry** (if applicable, of course). If your research design doesn't control for **compensatory rivalry**, you need to point out that this is one of the limitations of your study that will be discussed further in Section 9—the section where you pay attention to how the internal validity threat of **compensatory rivalry** directly affects the interpretation of your study's findings.
131	**Yes No** 🙂 🙁	Check to see that you have clearly stated how the research design you have finally selected for your proposed research study controls for one of the threats to internal validity: **demoralization** (if applicable, of course). If your research design doesn't control for **demoralization**, you need to point out that this is one of the limitations of your study that will be discussed further in Section 9—the section where you pay attention to how the internal validity threat of **demoralization** directly affects the interpretation of your study's findings.

132	**Yes No** ☺ ☹	Check to see that you have clearly stated how the research design you have finally selected for your proposed research study controls for one of the threats to external validity: **pretest-treatment interaction** (if applicable, of course). If your research design doesn't control for **pretest-treatment interaction**, you need to point out that this is one of the limitations of your study that will be discussed further in Section 9—the section where you pay attention to how the external validity threat of **pretest-treatment interaction** directly affects the interpretation of your study's findings.
133	**Yes No** ☺ ☹	Check to see that you have clearly stated how the research design you have finally selected for your proposed research study controls for one of the threats to external validity: **selection-treatment interaction** (if applicable, of course). If your research design doesn't control for **selection-treatment interaction**, you need to point out that this is one of the limitations of your study that will be discussed further in Section 9—the section where you pay attention to how the external validity threat of **selection-treatment interaction** directly affects the interpretation of your study's findings.

134	Yes No	Check to see that you have clearly stated how the research design you have finally selected for your proposed research study controls for one of the threats to external validity: **specificity of variables** (if applicable, of course). If your research design doesn't control for **specificity of variables**, you need to point out that this is one of the limitations of your study that will be discussed further in Section 9—the section where you pay attention to how the external validity threat of **specificity of variables** directly affects the interpretation of your study's findings.
135	Yes No	Check to see that you have clearly stated how the research design you have finally selected for your proposed research study controls for one of the threats to external validity: **reactive effects** (if applicable, of course). If your research design doesn't control for **reactive effects**, you need to point out that this is one of the limitations of your study that will be discussed further in Section 9—the section where you pay attention to how the external validity threat of **reactive effects** directly affects the interpretation of your study's findings.

136	**Yes** ☺ **No** ☹	Check to see that you have clearly stated how the research design you have finally selected for your proposed research study controls for one of the threats to external validity: **multiple-treatment interference** (if applicable, of course). If your research design doesn't control for **multiple-treatment interference**, you need to point out that this is one of the limitations of your study that will be discussed further in Section 9—the section where you pay attention to how the external validity threat of **multiple-treatment interference** directly affects the interpretation of your study's findings.
137	**Yes** ☺ **No** ☹	Check to see that you have clearly stated how the research design you have finally selected for your proposed research study controls for one of the threats to external validity: **researcher bias** (if applicable, of course). If your research design doesn't control for **researcher bias**, you need to point out that this is one of the limitations of your study that will be discussed further in Section 9—the section where you pay attention to how the external validity threat of **researcher bias** directly affects the interpretation of your study's findings.
138	**Yes** ☺ **No** ☹	Check to see that you have made explicit any assumptions that your research design rests upon.
139	**Yes** ☺ **No** ☹	Check to see that you have the skills to carry out the research design you have selected.

BOX 8a.1

Example of a Research Design Section from an Article
That Appeared in a Professional Journal

Evaluation of a Program to Educate Disadvantaged Parents to Enhance Child Learning[1]

A one-group pretest–posttest (*O-X-O*) design was employed to test the hypotheses that gains would be made in child learning as well as in parental social support and self-efficacy and that child behavior problems and parenting stress would be reduced upon completion of the program.

_____

[1]Leung, C., Tsang, S., & Dean, S. (2010). Evaluation of a program to educate disadvantaged parents to enhance child learning. *Research on Social Work Practice, 20*, 591–599.

BOX 8a.2

Example of a Research Design Section (and Sample Section) from
an Article That Appeared in a Professional Journal

Readiness for College Engagement among Students Who Have Aged Out of Foster Care[1]

METHOD

The convenience sample for this exploratory cross-sectional survey was 81 former foster youth who graduated from high school and were admitted as freshman in the 2009 (*n* = 35) and 2010 (*n* = 46) fall semesters. Participants were identified by their enrollment in the Seita Scholars Program.

_____

[1]Unrau, Y.A., Font, S.A., & Rawls, G. (2012). Readiness for college engagement among students who have aged out of foster care. *Children and Youth Services Review, 34*, 76–83.

BOX 8a.3

Example of a Research Design Section from a Research Proposal

**Chatham-Kent Children's Services (CKCS) Help-Seeking
Project for Adolescents in Out-of-Home Placement:
A Research Proposal[1]**

RESEARCH DESIGN

An experimental classical two-group pretest-posttest design will be utilized in this study with two follow-up points. All participants will be randomly assigned to either the experimental or the control condition of the study. Random assignment will continue until 60 youth have been assigned to each group (N = 120).

The figure below illustrates the basic layout of the research design. More specifically, it shows that the experimental group will receive the three-part intervention (described earlier) while the control group will not. It also shows that data will be collected from youth in both groups at four time points (i.e., study onset, 5 weeks, 10 weeks, 20 weeks), and the amount of remuneration (i.e., $10, $15, $20, $30) that each youth will receive for participating at each data collection point.

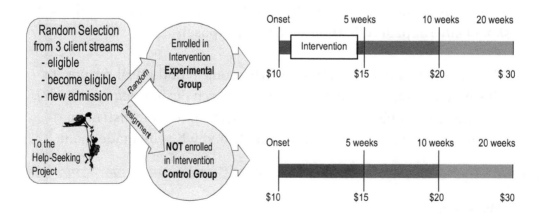

---

[1]Unrau, Y., & Grinnell, R.M., Jr. (2005). *Chatham-Kent Children's Services (CKCS) Help-Seeking Project for Adolescents in Out-of-Home Placement: A Research Proposal.* Submitted to Provincial Centre of Excellence for Child and Youth Mental Health at CHEO. Ottawa, Ontario, Canada K1H 8L1.

   Homework Assignment 8a.1

Writing Research Design Sections for Research Proposals

Boxes 8a.1 and 8a.2 present two Research Design sections from two different social work journal articles. Download and read one of the articles. Now that you are familiar with the research study depicted in the article you selected:

In the white space below, write a Research Design section you feel the authors *should have* written for the research proposal their study was based upon. The box will expand as you type.

NOTE: You do not have a copy of the authors' research proposal. You only have a copy of the article that resulted from the implementation of their proposal. Your main objective is to edit, revise, rearrange, and/or modify the authors' published Research Design section as you think it *should have* appeared in their research proposal.

• Use all the tips in this section to write your hypothetical proposal's Research Design section (e.g., is the research design clearly stated?).
• Submit your revised Research Design section to your instructor, pointing out all the revisions you made and why you made them.

Your Name(s):
Your Identification Number(s) (if any):
Assignment 8a.1. Title of Selected Article:

Type your revised Research Design section here.
(Box will automatically expand as you type)

　Homework Assignment 8a.2　　

Writing Research Design Sections for Research Proposals

Box 8a.3 presents a Research Design section from a research proposal.

In the white space below, write a Research Design section you feel the authors *should have* written for the research proposal. The box will expand as you type. Your main objective is to edit, revise, rearrange, and/or modify the authors' Research Design section in an effort to make it clearer, more concise, and easier to read and follow.

- Use all the tips in this section to rewrite your Research Design section (e.g., the specific research design is clearly stated).

- Submit your revised Research Design section to your instructor, pointing out all the revisions you made and why you made them.

Your Name(s):

Your Identification Number(s) (if any):

Assignment 8a.2

Type your revised Research Design section here.

(Box will automatically expand as you type)

Section 8a
Writing a Research Design Section for Your Research Proposal

Write a Research Design section for your research proposal in the white space provided below. The box will expand as you type.

- Use all the tips in this section to write your Research Design section (e.g., is it clear what research design is being used?).
- If possible, show your Research Design section to your classmates for their feedback.
- Revise your Research Design section based on your classmates' feedback.
- Submit your Research Design section to your instructor for comments.

Your Name(s):

Your Identification Number(s) (if any):

Title of Your Research Proposal:

Type your Research Design section here.
(Box will automatically expand as you type)

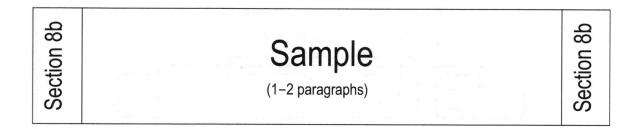

Sample
(1–2 paragraphs)

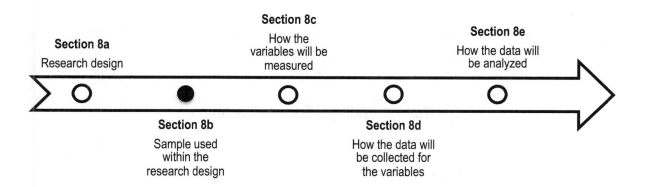

Section 8a

Research design

Section 8c

How the variables will be measured

Section 8e

How the data will be analyzed

Section 8b

Sample used within the research design

Section 8d

How the data will be collected for the variables

Solving the Problem

Now that you have selected the research design you propose to use in your study (Section 8a), you need to select a sampling strategy that you will use to select your research participants. These research participants will be the folks who supply you with the data you will need to answer your research question (or test your hypothesis). Obviously, not all research studies use humans in their samples. For example, they can use case files or existing databases.

As you know from your research methods book, samples that are used within research studies can be categorized into two general types: (1) probability and (2) nonprobability.

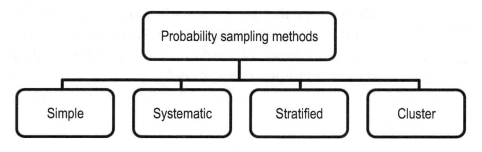

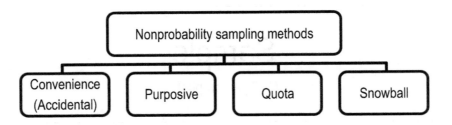

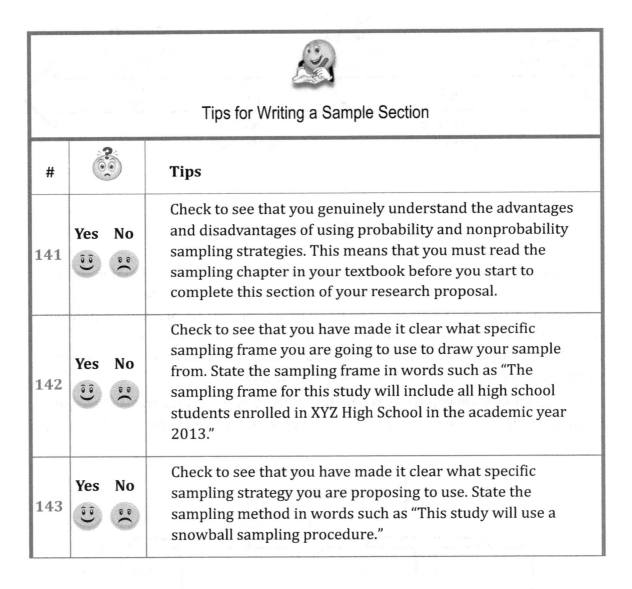

#		Tips
141	**Yes No** 😊 ☹	Check to see that you genuinely understand the advantages and disadvantages of using probability and nonprobability sampling strategies. This means that you must read the sampling chapter in your textbook before you start to complete this section of your research proposal.
142	**Yes No** 😊 ☹	Check to see that you have made it clear what specific sampling frame you are going to use to draw your sample from. State the sampling frame in words such as "The sampling frame for this study will include all high school students enrolled in XYZ High School in the academic year 2013."
143	**Yes No** 😊 ☹	Check to see that you have made it clear what specific sampling strategy you are proposing to use. State the sampling method in words such as "This study will use a snowball sampling procedure."

Tips for Writing a Sample Section

	Yes	No	
144	☺	☹	Check to see that you have made a clear connection between the sampling method you are proposing to use (Section 8b) and your research design (Section 8a).
145	☺	☹	Check to see that you have clearly stated the projected size (N) of your proposed sample.
146	☺	☹	Check to see that the overall size of your proposed sample is adequate to answer your research question (or to test your hypothesis).
147	☺	☹	Check to see that you have explained how you have determined the size and type of the sample you are going to be using, including the relative importance of Type I error (false positive) and Type II error (false negative).
148	☺	☹	Check to see that it is realistically feasible for you to obtain the necessary number of research participants for your proposed study.
149	☺	☹	Check to see that you have the support of your potential research participants to move ahead with your project.
150	☺	☹	Check to see that you have included specific relevant information on the population (your potential research participants) that you intend to focus on.
151	☺	☹	Check to see that your proposed sample will be representative of the population from which you will be drawing it. That is, you need to ask the question, "How representative will my sample be?"

152	Yes No	Check to see that you have made arrangements to write informed consent (and/or assent) letters to potential research participants. Copies of these documents are placed in your appendixes (e.g., Appendixes E and F in this book).
153	Yes No	Check to see that you have provided the specific instructions that your human research participants will receive in reference to how they will provide the data requested of them. Place a copy of the instructions in the appendixes (e.g., Appendixes H and/or I in this book).
154	Yes No	Check to see that you have the skills to carry out your selected sampling strategy. If not, obtain the skills before you start your sampling procedures.
155	Yes No	Check to see that you have made explicit any assumptions that your sampling strategy rests upon.
156	Yes No	Check with your research instructor to see if he/she has any examples of Sample sections from other research proposals to show you.

BOX 8b.1

Example of a Sample Section from a Research Proposal

**Chatham-Kent Children's Services (CKCS) Help-Seeking
Project for Adolescents in Out-of-Home Placement:
A Research Proposal[1]**

RESEARCH SETTING AND SAMPLE

The study will take place at Chatham-Kent Children's Services (CKCS), which has since 1996 operated as an amalgamated agency offering child protection, children's mental health, and child development/prevention services to children and families living in the Chatham-Kent Municipality. The agency, which is funded by the Ministry of Children and Youth Services, the Municipality of Chatham-Kent, the United Way, and others, was recently recommended for accreditation with Ontario Association of Children's Aid Societies and Children's Mental Health Ontario. The agency's mission statement is: "Working with our community to strengthen families and promote the well being and safety of children and youth," and the values of the agency clearly communicate that children are the priority of service delivery.

Random Selection from the Population

Eligibility criteria for study participation include: (1) 12 to 17 years old and living in out-of-home placement with CKCS during the period of the study, (2) discharge from care is not expected to occur within 20 weeks, (3) youth do not have severe cognitive delays or IQ scores less than 80, and (4) youth do not have severe medical needs or physical disabilities that would prevent them from participating in a group session with peers or having a 30-minute telephone conversation. Participants for the study will be selected from three streams of clientele at CKCS.

- *Eligible*: At the start point of the study, CKCS will have approximately 140 adolescents meeting the above eligibility criteria in care. About one-half of these adolescents are placed in foster homes, one-third in group homes, and one-fifth have room-and-board living arrangements.

- *Become Eligible*: Over a 21-month period of time CKCS estimates that approximately 26 children already in care at the start of the study will become eligible for participation as they pass their 12th birthdays.

- *New Admissions:* Over a 21-month period of time CKCS estimates that another 30 new admissions (meeting the eligibility criteria above) will enter CKCS out-of-home placements.

Study participants will be selected from the three streams of clientele just mentioned: (1) 64 study participants will be randomly selected from a list of eligible youth that are in CKCS care at the start of the study, (2) approximately 26 youth who have their 12th birthdays during the course of the study will be added to the sample as they become eligible for participation along with another 30 eligible youth entering out-of-home placement with CKCS during the study period. It is important to note that study participants ($N = 120$) will be randomly assigned to experimental or control groups with $N = 60$ per group.

Approach to Recruitment

Youth will be invited to participate in the study using informed consent procedures, which have received the approval of both the Research Ethics and Review Committee at CKCS and the Human Subject Institutional Review Board at Western Michigan University.

In sum, the project manager will be trained by the researchers to follow protocols for seeking informed consent from selected participants. These procedures include: informing youth about the details of the study—including incentives, explaining that participation is voluntary, and making it clear that there is no penalty for not participating.

---

[1]Unrau, Y., & Grinnell, R.M., Jr. (2005). *Chatham-Kent Children's Services (CKCS) Help-Seeking Project for Adolescents in Out-of-Home Placement: A Research Proposal.* Submitted to Provincial Centre of Excellence for Child and Youth Mental Health at CHEO. Ottawa, Ontario, Canada K1H 8L1.

BOX 8b.2

Example of a Sample Section from an Article That Appeared in a
Professional Journal

**Feasibility of Using Virtual Reality to Assess
Nicotine Cue Reactivity during Treatment[1]**

SAMPLING PROCEDURE

Participants ($n = 46$) were recruited through advertisements in a local paper in the
Atlanta metropolitan area and were involved in a treatment study. The following
were the inclusion criteria for study participation: (a) cigarette smokers with
current Diagnostic and Statistical Manual, Fourth Edition, Text Revision (DSM-IV-
TR; American Psychiatric Association, 2000) diagnosis of nicotine dependence,
who were daily smokers for the past 2 years; and (b) good physical health and
willing to wear a nicotine patch.

The following were exclusion criteria: (a) current DSM-IV-TR (American
Psychiatric Association, 2000) psychiatric diagnosis of chronic, severe mental
illness (e.g., schizophrenia, bipolar disorder, depression with psychosis, and
schizoaffective disorder), or substance abuse other than nicotine dependence; (b)
treated with any smoking cessation, (c) history of serious medical conditions (e.g.,
heart condition); (d) fear of closed spaces or visual problems that may impair
ability to view VR materials.

REFERENCE

American Psychiatric Association (2000). *Diagnostic and statistical manual of mental
disorders* (4th ed., Text Revision). Washington, DC: Author.

---

[1]Kaganoff, E., Bordnick, P.S., & Carter, B.L. (2012). Feasibility of using virtual reality to
assess nicotine cue reactivity during treatment. *Research on Social Work Practice, 22,* 159–
165.

BOX 8b.3

Example of a Sample Section from an Article That Appeared in a Professional Journal

**Motivations, Values, and Conflict Resolution:
Students' Integration of Personal and Professional Identities[1]**

Participants consisted of students currently enrolled in a MSW program at a private, Midwestern university. An e-mail describing the study was sent to all MSW students, and interested students were asked to contact the researcher directly. A nonrandom, purposive, maximum variation-sampling frame was used. Maximum-variation sampling involves selecting participants who vary widely along dimensions of interest (Patton, 2001). Dimensions of interest were religious affiliation, age, gender, sexual orientation, race, and family socioeconomic status. Interested students who did not identify with majority-group characteristics (Caucasian, heterosexual, and female) were automatically selected for participation.

Interested students who did identify with these majority-group demographics were further evaluated according to age and religious affiliation and enrolled based on the overall contribution to the maximum variation of the sample. Purposive recruitment attempts were made to students known to self-identify as male, non-Caucasian, and/or nonheterosexual. In line with Glaser and Strauss' (1967) idea of theoretical sampling, active recruitment of advanced students was initiated when a pattern encompassing differences among foundation students, advanced standing students, and concentration students began to emerge. Based on additional recruitment efforts, seven more participants were enrolled, yielding a total sample of 20 interviewees.

REFERENCES

Glaser, B.G., & Strauss, A.L. (1967). *The discovery of grounded theory: Strategies for qualitative research.* Hawthorne, NY: Aldine de Gruyter.

Patton, M. Q. (2001). *Qualitative research and evaluation methods* (3rd ed.). Thousand Oaks, CA: Sage.

———

[1]Osteene, P.J. (2011). Motivations, values, and conflict resolution: students' integration of personal and professional identities. *Journal Social Work Education, 47,* 423–444.

BOX 8b.4

Example of a Sample Section from an Article That Appeared in a Professional Journal

**Measuring Parenting Practices among Parents
of Elementary School–Age Youth[1]**

SAMPLING PROCEDURE

The study used data from a point in time, self-reported survey of parents (n = 1,153) with children under <11 years of age who were randomly selected from a population of parents residing in a southeastern state in 2007. Respondents resided in one of the eight counties in urban, suburban, and rural areas of the state. The counties were selected through a stratified process based on population density and region. Within each county, parents were randomly selected from the American Student List database of eligible parents.

---

[1]Randolph, K.A., & Radey, M. (2011). Measuring parenting practices among parents of elementary school–age youth. *Research on Social Work Practice, 21,* 88–97.

 Homework Assignment 8b.1

Writing Sample Sections for Research Proposals

Box 8b.1 presents a Sample section from a research proposal.

In the white space below, write a Sample section you feel the authors *should have* written for their research proposal. The box will expand as you type. Your main objective is to edit, revise, rearrange, and/or modify the authors' Sample section in an effort to make it clearer, more concise, and easier to read and follow.

- Use all the tips in this section to rewrite your Sample section (e.g., the specific sampling strategy is clearly stated).
- Submit your revised Sample section to your instructor, pointing out all the revisions you made and why you made them.

Your Name(s):

Your Identification Number(s) (if any):

Assignment 8b.1

Type your revised Sample section here.

(Box will automatically expand as you type)

Homework Assignment 8b.2

Writing Sample Sections for Research Proposals

Boxes 8b.2 to 8b.4 present three Sample sections from three different social work journal articles. Download and read one of the articles. Now that you are familiar with the research study depicted in the article you selected:

In the white space below, write a Sample section you feel the authors *should have* written for the research proposal their study was based upon. The box will expand as you type.

NOTE: You do not have a copy of the authors' research proposal. You only have a copy of the article that resulted from the implementation of their proposal. Your main objective is to edit, revise, rearrange, and/or modify the authors' published Sample section as you think it *should have* appeared in their research proposal.

- Use all the tips in this section to write your hypothetical proposal's Sample section (e.g., is the research design clearly stated?).
- Submit your revised Sample section to your instructor, pointing out all the revisions you made and why you made them.

Your Name(s):
Your Identification Number(s) (if any):
Assignment 8b.2. Title of Selected Article:

Type your revised Sample section here.
(Box will automatically expand as you type)

Section 8b
Writing a Sample Section for Your Research Proposal

Write a Sample section for your research proposal in the white space provided below. The box will expand as you type.

- Use all the tips in this section to write your Sample section (e.g., is it clear what sampling strategy is being used?).
- If possible, show your Sample section to your classmates for their feedback.
- Revise your Sample section based on your classmates' feedback.
- Submit your Sample section to your instructor for comments.

Your Name(s):

Your Identification Number(s) (if any):

Title of Your Research Proposal:

Type your Sample section here.
(Box will automatically expand as you type)

INSTRUMENTATION

(1 paragraph for each variable measured)

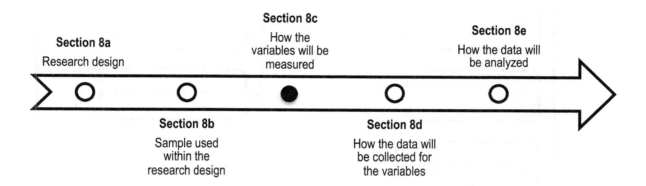

Section 8a

Research design

Section 8b

Sample used
within the
research design

Section 8c

How the
variables will be
measured

Section 8d

How the data will
be collected for
the variables

Section 8e

How the data will
be analyzed

Solving the Problem

Every variable contained within Section 7 has to be measured. Now comes the moment of truth: How are you going to measure them? That is the purpose of Section 8c.

As you know from your research methods text, there are many ways you can measure variables, commonly referred to as *instrumentation* in research lingo. In reality, you will always measure your variables by standardized and/or unstandardized measuring instrument(s) of some kind or another.

As a last resort, you can even make up your own measuring instrument such as a mailed survey or interview schedule. As you know from your research methods text, you should always use an existing standardized measuring instrument whenever possible, feasible, and practical.

The Instrumentation section of your proposal basically provides a visual copy of each measuring instrument that you propose to use for every variable contained in your research question (or hypothesis). If you are going to use a measuring

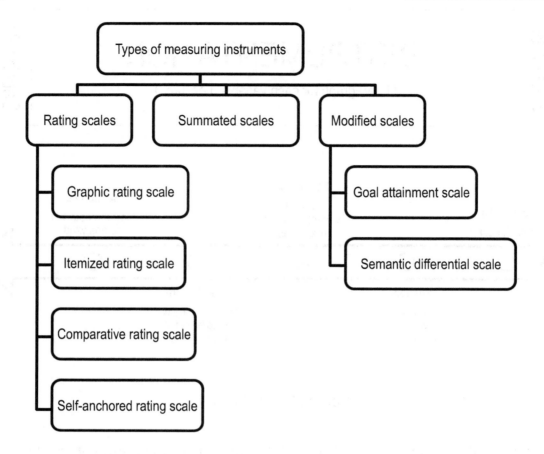

instrument that has been previously used in a study similar to yours, you will need to identify it by name, put a copy in your appendixes, and discuss its reliability and validity. If your measuring instrument is homegrown—that is, you are creating it yourself—you will need to outline the procedures you will take to develop and test its reliability and validity.

Copies of all your measuring instruments (whether standardized or homegrown) must be included in your appendixes—one appendix for each instrument (e.g., Appendix D in this book).

Tips for Writing an Instrumentation Section

#		Tips
156	Yes No	Check to see that you genuinely understand the advantages and disadvantages of the various ways to measure variables. This means that you must read the chapters on measurement and measuring instruments in your textbook!
157	Yes No	Check to see that you have made it clear which specific measuring instrument you are proposing to use for each variable in your study. State each measuring instrument in words such as "This study will use the *Problem Solving Inventory* to measure the problem-solving skills of the clients."
158	Yes No	Check to see that you have made a clear connection between the measuring instrument you are proposing to use (Section 8c), your research design (Section 8a), and most importantly, your variables contained within your Research Question (Section 7). After all, your measuring instruments will measure the variables contained within your research question (or hypothesis).

159	Yes No	Check to see that you have selected a standardized measurement instrument (if at all possible) to measure each of your variables. If you have selected a standardized measuring instrument, then be sure you have answers to basic questions about how the instrument used **research participants (sample)** in its construction. a. Are the samples representative of pertinent populations? b. Are the sample sizes sufficiently large? c. Are the samples homogeneous? d. Are the subsamples pertinent to respondents' demographics? e. Are the data obtained from the samples up to date?
160	Yes No	Check to see that you have selected a standardized measurement instrument (if at all possible) to measure each of your variables. If you have selected a standardized measuring instrument, then be sure you have answers to basic questions about the instrument's **validity**: a. Is the content domain clearly and specifically defined? b. Was there a logical procedure for including the items? c. Is the criterion measure relevant to the instrument? d. Was the criterion measure reliable and valid? e. Is the theoretical construct clearly and correctly stated? f. Do the scores converge with other relevant measures? g. Do the scores discriminate from irrelevant variables?

161	Yes No 🙂 ☹️	Check to see that you have selected a standardized measurement instrument (if at all possible) to measure each of your variables. If you have selected a standardized measuring instrument, then be sure you have answers to basic questions about the instrument's **reliability**: a. Is there sufficient evidence of internal consistency? b. Is there equivalence between various forms? c. Is there stability over a relevant time interval?
162	Yes No 🙂 ☹️	Check to see that you have selected a standardized measurement instrument (if at all possible) to measure each of your variables. If you have selected a standardized measuring instrument, then be sure you have answers to basic questions about the instrument's **practicality**: a. Is the instrument an appropriate length? b. Is the content socially acceptable to respondents? c. Is the instrument feasible to complete? d. Is the instrument relatively direct? e. Does the instrument have utility? f. Is the instrument relatively nonreactive? g. Is the instrument sensitive to measuring change? h. Is the instrument feasible to score?
163	Yes No 🙂 ☹️	Check to see that you have provided a short description for each measuring instrument in your proposal.
164	Yes No 🙂 ☹️	Check to see that your potential research participants have commented upon your proposed measuring instrument and how it's administered. That is, pilot test your measurements on some of your potential research participants to ascertain what they liked and did not like about your measurements and procedures.

165	Yes No 😊 ☹️	Check to see that you have included a copy of each measuring instrument in an individual appendix at the end of your proposal.
166	Yes No 😊 ☹️	Check to see that you have provided an explicit description of how to score the measuring instrument (see Appendix D as an example).
167	Yes No 😊 ☹️	Check to see that you have made explicit any assumptions that your measuring instruments rest upon.
168	Yes No 😊 ☹️	Check to see that you have the skills to actually administer the measuring instruments to your proposed research participants.
169	Yes No 😊 ☹️	Check with your research instructor to see if he/she has any examples of instrumentation sections from other research proposals to show you.

BOX 8c.1

Example of an Instrumentation Section from a Research Proposal

**Chatham-Kent Children's Services (CKCS) Help-Seeking
Project for Adolescents in Out-of-Home Placement:
A Research Proposal[1]**

INSTRUMENTATION

Data for the study will be collected through five self-report instruments that will be completed by youth in care, in addition to a case file review. Each instrument is summarized below.

1. The *Brief Child and Family Phone Interview (BCFPI)* is a computer-assisted, 30-

minute, clinical telephone interview. It is a key assessment instrument used by CKCS and other Ontario agencies that provide mental health services to children. The *BCFPI—Adolescent Version* provides risk assessment information about child functioning, as well as externalizing (i.e., impulsivity, cooperativeness, conduct) and internalizing (i.e., separation from parents, anxiety, mood) behaviors. The *BCFPI-Adolescent Version* is supported by reports of adequate reliability and validity (Cunningham, Pettingill, & Boyle, 2004). This instrument will measure youth demographic variables as well as youth mental health problems (a need factor in Andersen's Behavioral Health Model). A copy of this measuring instrument can be found in Appendix L.

2. The *Client Engagement in Child Protective Services (CECPS)* (Yatchmenoff, 2005) is composed of 19 items that are rated on a 5-point scale (5 = strongly agree to 1 = strongly disagree), with higher scores indicating higher engagement. Items assess four dimensions of client engagement in nonvoluntary child welfare services, which include receptivity, buy-in, working relationships, and mistrust.The *CECPS* is supported by sound reliability and construct validity (Yatchmenoff, 2005), and we have permission from the instrument's developer to modify the instrument for use with adolescents in our project. This instrument will measure youths' beliefs about the help available through Chatham-Kent Children's Service (CKCS), a predisposing factor in Andersen's Behavioral Health Model. A copy of this measuring instrument can be found in Appendix M.

3. The brief version of *Barriers to Adolescents Seeking Help (BASH)* (Kuhl, Jarkon-Horlick, & Morrissey, 1997; Wilson , Deane, Ciarrochi, & Rickwood, 2005) is composed of 11 items that target belief-based barriers to seeking help for psychological problems from mental health professionals. Each item is rated on a 6-point scale (1 = strongly disagree to 6 = strongly agree), and higher scores indicate more barriers. The instrument reports good internal consistency (r = .84) (Wilson, Deane, & Ciarrochi, 2005) and has been used in several research studies investigating help-seeking behavior of adolescents. This instrument will measure youths' barriers to help seeking (a predisposing factor). A copy of this measuring instrument can be found in Appendix N.

4. The *Barriers to Engagement in Treatment Screen (BETS)* (Wilson, Fogarty, & Deane, 2002) is composed of 11 items that measure specific barriers related to youths' engagement with their caseworkers. Each item is rated on a 4-point scale (0 = Agree to 3 = disagree), and higher scores indicate more barriers. The *BETS* has been used primarily as a screening tool, which is intended to facilitate discussion between youth and the service provider at the outset of treatment. Psychometrics for the *BETS* are currently being tested but show promising results (C.J. Wilson, personal communication, November, 2005). This instrument will measure the youths' engagement with CKCS workers (a predisposing

factor). A copy of this measuring instrument can be found in Appendix O.

5. The *General Help Seeking Questionnaire (GHSQ)* was developed by a group of Australian researchers (Deane, Wilson, & Ciarrochi, 2001; Wilson, Deane, Ciarrochi, & Rickwood, 2005) and is composed of 10 specific help sources. For each source, youth rate the likelihood of seeking help for suicidal thoughts and personal-emotional problems on a 7-point scale (1 = extremely unlikely to 7 = extremely likely). Higher scores indicate greater intention to seek help. The GHSQ is designed to allow modifications of the list of specific help sources so that language used will reflect job titles that are consistent with CKCS. Help-seeking intention is examined as a mean score per problem-type, and is well suited to measuring change in help-seeking intentions. The GHSQ is reported to have satisfactory reliability and validity (Wilson, Deane, Ciarrochi, & Rickwood, 2005), and good 3-week test-retest reliability for suicidal (r = .88) and personal-emotional (r = .86) problems (Wilson, Deane, & Ciarrochi, 2005). It has also been shown to relate to actual help-seeking in the past month, and to predict future help-seeking behaviors (Deane, Ciarrochi, Wilson, et al., 2001; Wilson, Deane, Ciarrochi, & Rickwood, 2005). This instrument will measure youths' intentions to seek help as well as actual requests for help (date of request and type of problem), which is the outcome or dependent variable of the study. A copy of this measuring instrument can be found in Appendix P.

6. *Case File Review:* Data collected from case files will be facilitated by use of a standard checklist recording form that will be specifically created for this study in order to promote consistency of data recording. Information gathered from case file information will include: demographic variables, placement characteristics, and additional documentation related to youths' requests for help from CKCS workers. A copy of this measuring instrument can be found in Appendix Q.

REFERENCES

Cunningham, C.E., Pettingill, P., & Boyle, M.H. (2004). *The Brief Child and Family Phone Interview Version 3: Interviewer's Manual.* Hamilton: BCFPI Works.

Deane, F.P., Wilson, C.J. & Ciarrochi, J. (2001). Suicidal ideation and help negation: Not just hopelessness or prior help. *Journal of Clinical Psychology, 57,* 901–914.

Deane, F.P., Wilson, C.J., Ciarrochi, J. & Rickwood, D. (2002). *Mental Health Help-Seeking in Young People.* Report to the National Health and Medical Research Council of Australia, Canberra, Australia, Grant YS060. Wollongong, NSW: University of Wollongong, Illawarra Institute for Mental Health.

Kuhl, J., Jarkon-Horlick, L., & Morrissel, R. F. (1997). Measuring barriers to help-seeking in adolescents. *Journal of Youth and Adolescence, 26,* 637–650.

Wilson, C.J., Deane, F.P., & Ciarrochi, J. (2005). Can hopelessness and adolescents' beliefs and attitudes about seeking help account for help negation? *Journal of Clinical Psychology, 61,* 1525–1539.

Wilson, C.J., Deane, F.P., Ciarrochi, J., & Rickwood, D. (2005). Measuring help-seeking intentions: Properties of the General Help-Seeking Questionnaire. *Canadian Journal of*

Counseling, 39, 15–28.

Wilson, C.J., Deane, F.P., & Fogarty, K. (2004). *GPs in schools: Building bridges to general practice* (2nd ed.). Participant training manual for "Youth Friendly" General Practitioners in strategies for classroom presentation and outreach. Illawarra Division of General Practice, Wollongong, Australia. Funded by the Commonwealth Department of Health and Aging.

Wilson, C.J., Fogarty, K., & Deane, F.P. (2002). *The essential youth friendly GP kit.* An evidence-based information and resource pack to increase GP competencies when dealing with young people. Illawarra Institute for Mental Health, University of Wollongong, Wollongong, Australia.

Yatchmenoff, D.K. (2005). Measuring client engagement from the client's perspective in nonvoluntary child protective services. *Research on Social Work Practice, 15*, 84–96.

---

[1]Unrau, Y., & Grinnell, R.M., Jr. (2005). *Chatham-Kent Children's Services (CKCS) Help-Seeking Project for Adolescents in Out-of-Home Placement: A Research Proposal.* Submitted to Provincial Centre of Excellence for Child and Youth Mental Health at CHEO. Ottawa, Ontario, Canada K1H 8L1.

BOX 8c.2

Example of an Instrumentation Section from an Article That Appeared in a Professional Journal

Evaluation of a Program to Educate Disadvantaged Parents to Enhance Child Learning[1]

MEASURES

The parent participants were requested to complete the following questionnaires before and after the HOPE program and midway through the program (Week 15):

1. The *Eyberg Child Behavior Inventory* (ECBI; Eyberg & Ross, 1978): a 36-item multidimensional measure of parental perception of disruptive behavior in children, which incorporates two scores, namely, the intensity and problem scores, the Chinese version of which was validated by Leung, Chan, Pang, and Cheng (2003).

2. The *Parenting Stress Index* (PSI; Lam, 1999): a 36-item questionnaire on issues related to parenting stress. Apart from the total score, three subscale scores can also be calculated, namely, Parental Distress (PD), Parent-Child Dysfunctional Interaction (PCDI), and Difficult Child (DC). The Chinese version of the scale was validated by Lam (1999).
3. The *General Self-Efficacy Scale* (Schwarzer, 1993): a 10-item scale measured on a 4-point Likert-type scale ranging from 1 (not at all true) to 4 (exactly true). A validated Chinese version is available (Zhang & Schwarzer, 1995).
4. The *Duke-UNC Functional Social Support Questionnaire* (Broadhead, Gehlbach, de Gruy, & Kaplan, 1988): an 8-item questionnaire on perceived social support in various areas. The questionnaire has been translated into Chinese using back translation, and it has been used with Chinese immigrants in Hong Kong with satisfactory reliability (.94; Leung et al., 2007).

REFERENCES

Broadhead, W.E., Gehlbach, S.H., de Gruy, F.V., & Kaplan, B.H. (1988). The Duke-UNC functional social support questionnaire: Measurement of social support in family medicine patients. *Medical Care, 26*, 709–723.

Eyberg, S.M., & Ross, A.W. (1978). Assessment of child behavior problems: The validation of a new inventory. *Journal of Clinical Psychology, 16,* 113–116.

Lam, D. (1999). Parenting stress and anger: The Hong Kong experience. *Child and Family Social Work, 4,* 337–346.

Leung, C.M., Chan, S.C.M., Pang, R.C.Y., & Cheng, W.K.C. (2003). *Validation of the Chinese version of the Eyberg Child Behavior Inventory for use in Hong Kong.* Unpublished manuscript, Education Bureau, Hong Kong.

Leung, C., Leung, S. S. L., & Chan, R. (2007). The adaptation of mainland Chinese immigrant parents of preschool children in Hong Kong. *E-Journal of Applied Psychology, 3,* 43–57. Retrieved from ttp://ojs.lib.swin.edu.au/index.php/ejap/article/view/79/106.

Schwarzer, R. (1993). *Measurement of perceived self-efficacy: Psychometric scales for cross-cultural research.* Berlin, Germany: Zentrale Universitats Druckerei der FU Berlin.

Zhang, J.X., & Schwarzer, R. (1995). Measuring optimistic self-beliefs: A Chinese adaptation of the General Self-Efficacy Scale. *Psychologia, 38,* 174–181.

---

[1]Leung, C., Tsang, S., & Dean, S. (2011). Evaluation of a program to educate disadvantaged parents to enhance child learning. *Research on Social Work Practice, 20,* 591–599.

Homework Assignment 8c.1

Writing Instrumentation Sections for Research Proposals

Box 8c.1 presents the Instrumentation section from a research proposal.

In the white space below, write an Instrumentation section you feel the authors *should have* written for the research proposal. The box will expand as you type. Your main objective is to edit, revise, rearrange, and/or modify the authors' Instrumentation section in an effort to make it clearer, more concise, and easier to read and follow.

- Use all the tips in this section to rewrite your Instrumentation section (e.g., is each instrument referred to in the appendix?).
- Submit your revised Instrumentation section to your instructor, pointing out all the revisions you made and why you made them.

Your Name(s):

Your Identification Number(s) (if any):

Assignment 8c.1

Type your revised Instrumentation section here.
(Box will automatically expand as you type)

Homework Assignment 8c.2

Writing Instrumentation Sections for Research Proposals

Box 8c.2 presents the Instrumentation section (Measures) from a social work journal article. Download and read the article. Now that you are familiar with the research study depicted in the article:

In the white space below, write an Instrumentation section you feel the authors *should have* written for the research proposal their study was based upon. The box will expand as you type.

NOTE: You do not have a copy of the authors' research proposal. You only have a copy of the article that resulted from the implementation of their proposal. Your main objective is to edit, revise, rearrange, and/or modify the authors' published Instrumentation section as you think it *should have* appeared in their research proposal.

- Use all the tips in this section to write your hypothetical proposal's Instrumentation section (e.g., is the research design clearly stated?).
- Submit your revised Instrumentation section to your instructor, pointing out all the revisions you made and why you made them.

Your Name(s):

Your Identification Number(s) (if any):

Assignment 8c.2

Type your revised Instrumentation (Measures) section here.

(Box will automatically expand as you type)

Section 8c
Writing an Instrumentation Section for Your Research Proposal

Write an Instrumentation section for your research proposal in the white space provided below. The box will expand as you type.

- Use all the tips in this section to write your Instrumentation section (e.g., is it clear how each variable is measured?).
- If possible, show your Instrumentation section to your classmates for their feedback.
- Revise your Instrumentation section based on your classmates' feedback.
- Submit your Instrumentation section to your instructor for comments.

Your Name(s):

Your Identification Number(s) (if any):

Title of Your Research Proposal:

Type your Instrumentation section here.

(Box will automatically expand as you type)

DATA COLLECTION

(1–2 paragraphs for each data collection method)

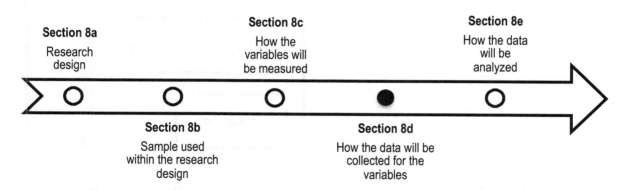

Section 8a

Research design

Section 8c

How the variables will be measured

Section 8e

How the data will be analyzed

Section 8b

Sample used within the research design

Section 8d

How the data will be collected for the variables

Solving the Problem

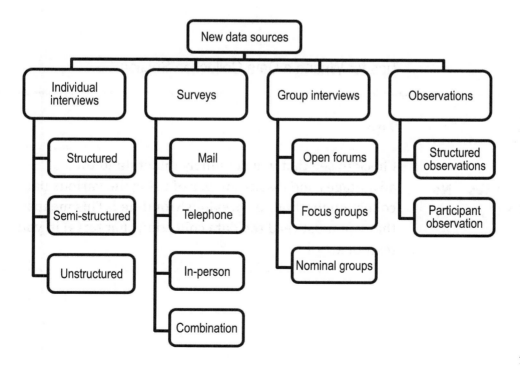

New data sources

Individual interviews
- Structured
- Semi-structured
- Unstructured

Surveys
- Mail
- Telephone
- In-person
- Combination

Group interviews
- Open forums
- Focus groups
- Nominal groups

Observations
- Structured observations
- Participant observation

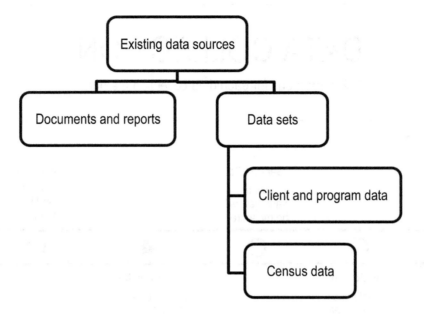

As you know from your research methods text, you can collect new data and/or existing data to answer your research question (or test your hypothesis).

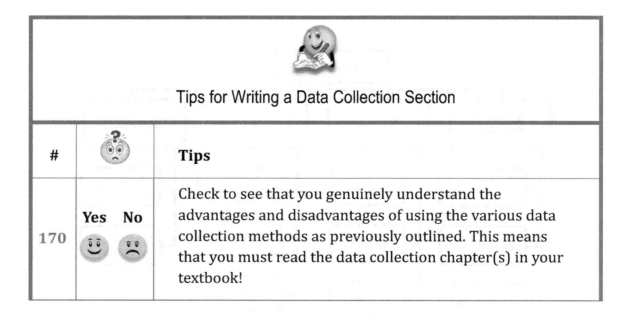

		Tips for Writing a Data Collection Section
#	❓	**Tips**
170	Yes ☺ No ☹	Check to see that you genuinely understand the advantages and disadvantages of using the various data collection methods as previously outlined. This means that you must read the data collection chapter(s) in your textbook!

171	Yes No	Check to see that you have made a clear connection between the measuring instrument you are proposing to use (Section 8c), your research design (Section 8a), your sample (Section 8b), and your data collection method.
172	Yes No	Check to see that you have made clear which specific data collection method(s) you are proposing to use in your study.
173	Yes No	Check to see that you have made a clear data-collection plan, as illustrated in Table 8d.1. Do not submit your proposal without such a plan.
174	Yes No	Check to see that you have covered all the necessary logistical considerations to collect data in the most efficient manner possible.
175	Yes No	Check to see that you have indicated how you will deal with those folks who do not respond, are unavailable, or refuse to respond to your questionnaire.
176	Yes No	Check to see that you have made explicit any assumptions that your data collection method(s) rest upon.
177	Yes No	Check to see that you have the skills to actually collect the data via your selected data collection method(s) for your proposed research study.
178	Yes No	Check with your research instructor to see if he/she has any examples of Data Collection sections from other research proposals to show you.

Table 8d.1

Example of a Data-Collection Plan for Two Variables

a	b	c	d	e	f	g
Indicator	How indicator is measured	Who provides the data	How data are gathered	When data are gathered	Where data are gathered	Who collects the data
Increase the self-esteem of pregnant adolescents after they have their babies	*Rosenberg Self-Esteem Scale* (Appendix Q)	Client	1. Self-administered 2. Self-administered 3. Self-administered	1. Intake 2. Exit interview 3. 3 months after intervention	1. Waiting room 2. Social worker's office 3. Client's home	1. Receptionist 2. Social Worker 3. Case-aid
Increase the social support systems of pregnant adolescents after they have their babies	*Scale of Perceived Social Support* (Appendix R)	Client	1. Self-administered 2. Self-administered in group setting 3. Self-administered in a group setting	1. Intake 2. Last day of intervention 3. 1 month after intervention	1. Waiting room 2. In last group session 3. Group interview in coffee shop	1. Receptionist 2. Group leader 3. Research assistant

a = This column is where you list specifically what indicator(s) you are going to use to measure each of your variables. Theoretically, you can have multiple indicators to measure the same variable.

b = This column is where you list specifically how you are going to measure each indicator in column *a*. For example, the indicators for self-esteem and social support can be measured by many different means. In our example, we chose one standardized measuring instrument for each variable: the *Rosenberg Self-Esteem Scale* for our self-esteem variable and the *Scale of Perceived Social Support* for our social support variable.

c = This column is where you list specifically who is going to provide the data, via the use of your selected measuring instrument (*b*). In a nutshell, this person, called a data source, is the one who is going to provide the data for the measuring instrument. Once again, a measuring instrument can be completed by a variety of different data sources.

d = This column is where you list specifically how the measuring instrument is going to be administered. Not only can you use a variety of measuring instruments to measure an indicator (*b*), but you also have a variety of options for how to administer them. For example, you can read the items or questions on the measuring instrument to your clients, or you can have your clients fill out the instrument themselves. You can also have clients complete them individually with no one around or in group settings such as parks, waiting rooms, and coffee shops.

e = This column is where you state the exact time frame in which the measuring instrument is going to be completed. Once again, there are many options available. For example, clients could complete measuring instruments at home on Friday nights before bedtime or at the beginning of your interview.

f = This column, which is highly related to the previous column (*e*), is where you list the specific location where the measuring instrument will be completed. For example, you can have your clients complete the *Rosenberg Self-Esteem Scale* in your program's waiting room, at home, or in your office.

g = This column is where you list specifically who is going to collect the data via the measuring instrument when it is completed. After the data source (*c*) has provided the data for the measuring instrument (*b*), who's going to collect the completed instrument for analysis? And, more importantly, who is going to collate all the data into a databank for further analyses?

BOX 8d.1

Example of a Quantitative Data Collection Section (and an Instrumentation Section) from a Research Proposal

Students' Persistence in the University of Nebraska at Lincoln: A Mixed Methods Study[1]

PHASE I: QUANTITATIVE DATA COLLECTION AND INSTRUMENTATION

The first, quantitative phase of the study will focus on identifying internal and external factors contributing to and/or impeding students' persistence in the ELHE-DE program. The cross-sectional survey design, which implies the data will be collected at one point in time (McMillan, 2000), will be used.

The primary technique for collecting the quantitative data will be a self-developed questionnaire, containing items of different formats: multiple choice, asking either for one option or all that apply, dichotomous answers like "Yes" and "No," self-assessment items, measured on the 7-point Likert-type, and open-ended questions. A panel of professors teaching in the ELHE-DE program was used to secure the content validity of the survey instrument. The questionnaire consists of 24 questions, which are organized into six sections or scales.

1. The first section of the survey asks questions related to the ELHE-DE program and participants' experiences in it. It includes the selection questions related to the status of subjects in the program and within each of the four groups, factors contributing to the decision to proceed or withdraw, UNL support services, and participants' experiences in the program. The latter are measured on a 7-point Likert-type scale from "Strongly disagree" to "Strongly agree" and will provide data regarding how the program-, faculty-, and institutional-related factors impact ELHE-DE students' persistence.

2. The second section will measure participants' comfort level with the online learning environment and will provide additional data about the impact of institutional-related factors. A 7-point rating scale from "Very uncomfortable" to "Very comfortable" is used.

3. The third section is focused on participants' experiences with their academic advisors and will provide data regarding the role of an advisor in pursuing the doctoral degree in CMAL. A 7-point rating scale from "Extremely negative" to "Extremely positive" is used.

4. The fourth section asks for self-evaluation of how motivated the students are to pursue doctoral degree via distributed means. The scale from 1 to 7, from "Strongly disagree" to "Strongly agree," is used.

5. The fifth section is focused on how selected external factors have influenced participants' progress in the program. This scale will provide data to answer the fifth research question. These experiences are measured on a 7-point Likert-type scale from "Strongly disagree" to "Strongly agree." Demographic questions constitute the sixth, final section of the questionnaire. They will provide information regarding participants' age, gender, employment, and Nebraska residency status, degrees earned, and family structure. Some questions in the survey have an open-ended "Other (specify)" option to provide one correct answer for every subject in the study. A choice of "Not applicable" (NA) is included, when necessary.

6. The last question on the survey is open-ended and will ask for additional information about students' experiences in the ELHE-DE program.

The survey questionnaire will be web-based and accessed through the URL, which will be sent to all current and former ELHE-DE students identified by the Department of Educational Administration. One of the advantages of web-based surveys is that participants' responses will automatically be stored in a database and can be easily transformed into numeric data in Excel or SPSS formats. Last known working e-mail addresses are available for all the potential participants in the study.

An informed consent form will be posted on the web as an opening page of the survey. Participants will click on the button below, saying, "I agree to complete this survey," thus expressing their compliance to participate in the study and complete the survey. The survey instrument will be pilot tested on the 5% randomly selected participants representing the former and current students in the ELHE-DE program. The goal of the pilot study is to validate the instrument and to test its reliability. All names from the eligible ELHE-DE participants identified in the database will be entered into the SPSS computer analysis system.

A random proportionate by group sample of 15 participants will be selected. These participants will be excluded from the subsequent major study. The results of the pilot survey will help establish stability and internal consistency reliability, face, and content validity of the questionnaire. Based on the pilot test results, the survey items will be revised if needed.

A week before the survey is available on the web, participants will receive a notification from the department about the importance of their input for the study. This will help escape a low response rate, which is typical for web-based surveys. To decrease the response rate error and solicit a relatively high response rate of the survey, a three-phase follow-up sequence will be used (Dillman, 2000).

To those subjects who will have not responded by the set date (1) five days after distributing the survey URL, an e-mail reminder will be sent out; (2) ten days later, the second e-mail reminder will be sent; (3) two weeks later, the third e-mail reminder will be sent stating the importance of the participant's input for the study.

REFERENCES

Dillman, D.A. (2000). *Mail and Internet surveys: The tailored design method* (2nd ed.). New York: John Wiley.

McMillan, J.H. (2000). *Educational research: Fundamentals for the consumer* (3rd ed.). New York: Addison Wesley Longman.

———————

[1]Ivankova, N.V. (2002). *Students' persistence in the University of Nebraska at Lincoln: A mixed methods study.* Doctoral dissertation proposal submitted for partial fulfillment of the requirements for the degree of Doctor of Philosophy. Graduate College at the University of Nebraska at Lincoln.

BOX 8d.2

Example of a Qualitative Data Collection Section
from a Research Proposal

Students' Persistence in the University of Nebraska at Lincoln: A Mixed Methods Study[1]

PHASE II: QUALITATIVE DATA COLLECTION

The second, qualitative phase in the study will focus on explaining the results of the statistical tests, obtained in the first, quantitative phase. The multiple case studies design (Stake, 1995) will be used for collecting and analyzing the qualitative data. A case study is a type of ethnographic design (Creswell, 2002; LeCompte & Schensul, 1999) and is an exploration of a "bounded system" or a case over time, through detailed, in-depth data collection involving multiple sources of information and rich in context (Merriam, 1988; Creswell & Maitta, 2002).

In this study, the instrumental multiple cases (Stake, 1995) will serve the purpose of "illuminating a particular issue" (Creswell, 2002, p. 485), such as persistence in the ELHE-DE program, and they will be described and compared to provide insight into an issue. The primary technique will be conducting in-depth semi-structured telephone interviews with four students, one from each group (Beginning, Matriculated, Graduated, and Withdrawn/Inactive). Individual interviews with the significant others of these selected participants might also be conducted. Triangulation of different data sources is important in case study analysis (Creswell, 1998). Academic transcripts will be used to validate the information obtained during the interviews.

The participants will be asked for consent to access their transcripts, while the information regarding the courses and grades will be received through the researcher's advisor. I will also ask participants to provide elicitation materials or physical artifacts that might have a relationship to their persistence or non-persistence in the ELHE-DE program. Selected online classes taken by the participants and archived on a Lotus Notes or Blackboard server will also be examined for supporting information.

The Interview Protocol will include 10 to 15 open-ended questions, and will be pilot tested. The content of the protocol questions will be grounded in the results of the statistical tests of the relationships between the participants' group membership and the predictor factors as related to students' persistence in the program, and will elaborate on them. The questions will focus on the issue of persistence in the ELHE-DE program and about the details of the cases selected on maximal variation principle. The protocol will be pilot tested on three students selected from the same target population, but then excluded from the full study.

Debriefing with the participants will be conducted to obtain information on the clarity of the interview questions and their relevance to the study aim. The participants will receive the interview questions prior to the scheduled calling time, and will be informed the interview will be tape-recorded and transcribed verbatim. Respondents will have an opportunity to review and, if necessary, correct the contents of the interview after it has been transcribed.

REFERENCES

Creswell, J.W. (1998). *Qualitative inquiry and research design: Choosing among five traditions.* Thousand Oaks, CA: Sage.

Creswell, J.W. (2002). *Educational research: Planning, conducting, and evaluating quantitative and qualitative approaches to research.* Upper Saddle River, NJ: Merrill/Pearson Education.

Creswell, J.W., & Maitta, R. (2002). Qualitative research. In N. Salkind (Ed.), *Handbook of research design and social measurement* (pp. 143–184). Thousand Oaks, CA: Sage.

LeCompte, M.D., & Schensul, J.J. (1999). *Designing and conducting ethnographic research. Ethnographer's Toolkit, 1.* Walnut Creek, CA: AltaMira.

Merriam, S.B. (1998). *Qualitative research and case study applications in education: Revised and expanded from case study research in education.* San Francisco, CA: Jossey-Bass.

Stake, R. E. (1995). *The art of case study research.* Thousand Oaks, CA: Sage.

---

[1]Ivankova, N.V. (2002). *Students' persistence in the University of Nebraska at Lincoln: A mixed methods study.* Doctoral dissertation proposal submitted for partial fulfillment of the requirements for the degree of Doctor of Philosophy. Graduate College at the University of Nebraska at Lincoln.

Homework Assignment 8d

Writing Data Collection Sections for Research Proposals

Boxes 8d.1 and 8d.2 present a Data Collection section from a research proposal. Box 8d.1 contains the quantitative data that are to be collected (Phase I), and Box 8d.2 describes how the qualitative data will be collected (Phase II).

In the white space below, write the two Data Collection sections (Phases I and II) you feel the author *should have* written for her research proposal. The box will expand as you type. Your main objective is to edit, revise, rearrange, and/or modify the author's Data Collection section in an effort to make it clearer, more concise, and easier to read and follow.

- Use all the tips in this section to rewrite your Data Collection section (e.g., how are nonresponses to be dealt with?).

- Submit your revised Data Collection section to your instructor, pointing out all the revisions you made and why you made them.

Your Name(s):
Your Identification Number(s) (if any):
Assignment 8d

Type your revised Data Collection section here.
(Box will automatically expand as you type)

Section 8d
Writing a Data Collection Section for Your Research Proposal

Write a Data Collection section for your research proposal in the white space provided below. The box will expand as you type.

- Use all the tips in this section to write your Data Collection section (e.g., did you construct a Data Collection table like Table 8d.1?).
- If possible, show your Data Collection section to your classmates for their feedback.
- Revise your Data Collection section based on your classmates' feedback.
- Submit your Data Collection section to your instructor for comments.

Your Name(s):

Your Identification Number(s) (if any):

Title of Your Research Proposal:

Type your Data Collection section here.

(Box will automatically expand as you type)

DATA ANALYSIS

(1–2 paragraphs for each data analysis method)

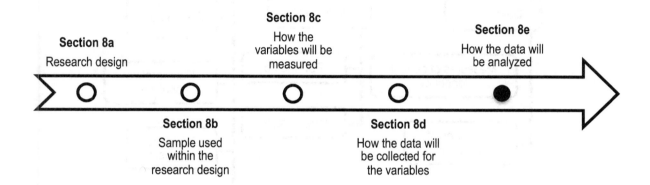

Section 8a

Research design

Section 8c

How the
variables will be
measured

Section 8e

How the data will
be analyzed

Section 8b

Sample used
within the
research design

Section 8d

How the data will
be collected for
the variables

Solving the Problem

As you know from your research methods text there are two general types of data analyses—quantitative and qualitative. In short, you can collect data for your study's variables in the form of numbers and/or words. Numbers are analyzed via quantitative methods and words by qualitative ones.

One of the most neglected areas of the average social work research proposal is that dealing with the collection of data and the resulting analysis and interpretation of them. Nevertheless, a major part of your proposed project will be spent analyzing and interpreting the data you have collected.

The type of data analysis you will use depends on whether you have collected quantitative and/or qualitative data. It is important to realize, however, that although that the data collection section and data analysis section are discussed separately in a research proposal, the sections are always written simultaneously.

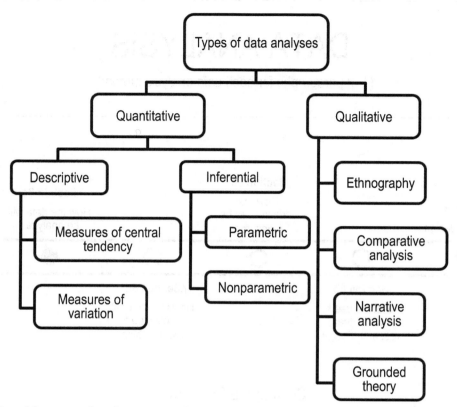

You should not make decisions about your data collection method (Section 8d) without also *simultaneously* deciding which data analysis method (Section 8e) you will use to analyze the data you have collected. In a nutshell, data collection and analysis go hand in hand.

Tips for Writing a Data Analysis Section

#		Tips
179	**Yes No**	Check to see that you know how to do simple quantitative and qualitative data analyses. This means that you must read the two or more chapters in your textbook that describe how to do these two types of data analyses!
180	**Yes No**	Check to see that you have made a clear connection between the measuring instrument(s) you are proposing to use (Section 8c), your research design (Section 8a), your data source(s) (Section 8d), your sample (Section 8d), and your data analysis plan.
181	**Yes No**	Check to see that you have made clear which specific data analysis method(s) you are proposing to use in your study.
182	**Yes No**	Check to see that you have indicated what attempts you will make to investigate possible sources of bias and their influence on your study's results.
183	**Yes No**	Check to see that you have covered how you will handle any missing data. That is, how will you handle the effects of research participants who do not complete all the data-gathering instruments or only complete portions of them?
184	**Yes No**	Check to see that you have stated in straightforward language how you will be handing your data analysis.

185	**Yes** ☺	**No** ☹	Check to see that you have made a clear data analysis plan, as illustrated in Table 8.e1. Your research proposal must contain a data-analysis table such as Table 8.e1.
186	**Yes** ☺	**No** ☹	Check to see that you have provided a well-thought-out rationale for your decision to use the data analysis you have selected.
187	**Yes** ☺	**No** ☹	Check to see that you have indicated the specific statistical software packages you plan to use when you analyze your data (e.g., AM Software from American Institutes for Research, Bascula from Statistics Netherlands, CENVAR from U.S. Bureau of the Census, CLUSTERS from University of Essex, Epi Info from Centers for Disease Control, Generalized Estimation System (GES) from Statistics Canada, IVEware from University of Michigan, PCCARP from Iowa State University, R survey package from the R Project, SAS/STAT from SAS Institute, SPSS from SPSS Inc., Stata from Stata Corporation, SUDAAN from Research Triangle Institute, VPLX from U.S. Bureau of the Census, WesVar from Westat, Inc.).
188	**Yes** ☺	**No** ☹	Check to see that you have used the appropriate statistic with each one of your hypotheses (if any).
189	**Yes** ☺	**No** ☹	Check to see that you have provided sample charts, graphs, or tables that will show how your data will be organized and reported in your final paper. It's always a great idea to create fake tables (with appropriate titles and headings) as templates you can use when you enter the data into them.
190	**Yes** ☺	**No** ☹	Check to see that you have made explicit any assumptions that your data analyses method(s) rest upon.

191	**Yes** 🙂 **No** 🙁	Check to see that you have the skills to actually analyze the data for your study.
192	**Yes** 🙂 **No** 🙁	Check with your research instructor to see if he/she has any examples of Data Analyses sections from other research proposals to show you.

Table 8e.1

Example of a Data-Analysis Plan for One Variable

Measured before and after Treatment

a	*b*	*c*	*d*	*e*
Name of variable	*Name of measuring instrument*	*Measurement* level	*When data are going to be collected*	*How data are going to be analyzed*
Self-Esteem	*Index of Self-Esteem* (Appendix D)	Ordinal (treated as interval)	Time 1: Intake interview Time 2: Exit interview	• Descriptive statistics • One group *t*-test between Time 1 and Time 2 scores

BOX 8e.1

Example of a Data Analysis Section from a Research Proposal

Chatham-Kent Children's Services (CKCS) Help-Seeking Project for Adolescents in Out-of-Home Placement: A Research Proposal[1]

DATA ANALYSIS PLAN

The first step in the analysis will be to generate descriptive statistics for all variables included in the study. Subsequently, we will examine preliminary relationships between each of the independent and total scores of the dependent variables using appropriate bivariate tests. Our primary interest is determining whether the experimental intervention has a positive impact on two particular dependent variables—(1) youths' requests for help from a CKCS worker (mental health or child protection) and (2) youths' intentions to seek help from others.

Since we expect to find statistically significant relationships between other independent variables and the dependent variables, we will proceed with multivariate analysis. Specifically, Poisson or zero-inflated regression will be used to test for differences between the experimental and control groups for count variables (e.g., number of times help requested), while event-history analysis (Cox regression) will be used to investigate differences in time-to-first request for help (Hypothesis #1). Analysis of covariance will be used to investigate differences between groups in terms of youths' intentions to seek help from others (Hypothesis #2).

---

[1]Unrau, Y., & Grinnell, R.M., Jr. (2005). *Chatham-Kent Children's Services (CKCS) Help-Seeking Project for Adolescents in Out-of-Home Placement: A Research Proposal.* Submitted to Provincial Centre of Excellence for Child and Youth Mental Health at CHEO. Ottawa, Ontario, Canada K1H 8L1.

BOX 8e.2

Example of a Data Analysis Section from an Article That Appeared in a Professional Journal

Vida Alegre:
Preliminary Findings of a Depression Intervention
for Immigrant Latino Mothers[1]

ANALYSIS

Due to the small sample size, nonparametric techniques were used. Among nonparametric techniques, we conducted a Wilcoxon signed-rank test to assess the magnitude of the change in the CES-D test scores at different points in time. Similar to the paired samples *t* test, the signed-rank test examines whether we can reject the null hypothesis that no significant difference exists between the pretest and posttest scores and the pretest and follow-up scores. However, unlike other nonparametric statistics, the Wilcoxon test also assesses the magnitude of any difference that might occur. The *Statistical Package for the Social Sciences* (SPSS) was used to produce the Wilcoxon test, which calculated the number of positive and negative differences, the *Z* score, and the associated probability level. The outcome thus allows an analysis of the direction and magnitude of change.

[1]Piedra, L.M., & Byoun, S. (2012). Vida alegre: Preliminary findings of a depression intervention for immigrant Latino mothers. *Research on Social Work Practice, 22*, 138–150.

 Homework Assignment 8e.1

Writing Data Analysis Sections for Research Proposals

Box 8e.1 presents a Data Analysis section from a research proposal.

In the white space below, write a Data Analysis section you feel the authors *should have* written for the research proposal. The box will expand as you type. Your main objective is to edit, revise, rearrange, and/or modify the authors' Data Analysis section in an effort to make it clearer, more concise, and easier to read and follow.

- Use all the tips in this section to rewrite your Data Analysis section (e.g., is each instrument referred to in the appendix?).
- Submit your revised Data Analysis section to your instructor, pointing out all the revisions you made and why you made them.

Your Name(s):

Your Identification Number(s) (if any):

Assignment 8e.1

Type your revised Data Analysis section here.
(Box will automatically expand as you type)

Homework Assignment 8e.2

Writing Data Analysis Sections for Research Proposals

Box 8e.2 presents the Data Analysis section from a social work journal article. Download and read the article. Now that you are familiar with the research study depicted in the article:

In the white space below, write a Data Analysis section you feel the authors *should have* written for the research proposal their study was based upon. The box will expand as you type.

NOTE: You do not have a copy of the authors' research proposal. You only have a copy of the article that resulted from the implementation of their proposal. Your main objective is to edit, revise, rearrange, and/or modify the authors' published Data Analysis section as you think it *should have* appeared in their research proposal.

- Use all the tips in this section to write your hypothetical proposal's Data Analysis section (e.g., is the research design clearly stated?).

- Submit your revised Data Analysis section to your instructor, pointing out all the revisions you made and why you made them.

Your Name(s):
Your Identification Number(s) (if any):
Assignment 8e.2

Type your revised Data Analysis section here.
(Box will automatically expand as you type)

Section 8e
Writing a Data Analysis Section for Your Research Proposal

Write a Data Analysis section for your research proposal in the white space provided below. The box will expand as you type.

- Use all the tips in this section to write your Data Analysis section (e.g., Is Table 8e.1 fully completed and done correctly?)
- If possible, show your Data Analysis section to your fellow classmates for their feedback.
- Revise your Data Analysis section based on your classmates' feedback.
- Submit your Data Analysis section to your instructor for comments.

Your Name(s):

Your Identification Number(s) (if any):

Title of Your Research Proposal:

Type your Data Analysis section here.
(Box will automatically expand as you type)

PART V
Evaluating the Proposed Solution

It's now time to evaluate the first eight sections of your research proposal, to delineate your study's limitations and significance.

All research proposals (and, of course, the findings that are ultimately derived from them) have limitations. This includes your proposed study as well. Section 9 gives you the opportunity to inform your readers that you know what your study's limitations are.

It's also the time to discuss the overall practical and/or theoretical merits of your study. As you know, you briefly suggested the study's significance in two previous sections: Abstract and Introduction. Section 10 is where you expand on your study's overall significance to the social work profession.

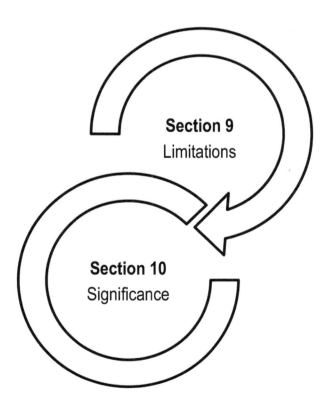

Section 9
Limitations

Section 10
Significance

LIMITATIONS

(1–3 sentences for each important point)

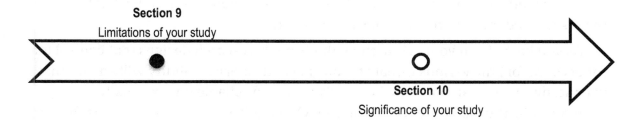

Section 9
Limitations of your study

Section 10
Significance of your study

Evaluating the Proposed Solution

A *limitation* is a weakness of your proposed study, and all research studies have them—and that includes yours! Think, for a moment, about your overall research design, your sample, the measuring instruments you are going to use, and your data collection and analysis plans.

Think about all the threats to internal and external validity that may have been impossible for you to avoid or even minimize. You need to explain to the readers that you know what your study's limitations are. Simple examples of limitations might include the following:

1. Due to the small availability, nonrandom sample that I want to use, my results will not be generalizable beyond the specific population from which I'm going to draw my sample.

2. Because some of my randomly selected research participants may not respond to my questionnaire, my results may not accurately reflect the opinions of all members within my sampling frame.

3. Due to the 3-year duration of my study, a significant number of my research participants who were available at the beginning of my study may not be available (or may be unwilling to participate) in the final stage of my study.

Scrupulously stating all the limitations of your study will help your readers understand some of the fundamental problems you will probably encounter when you actually perform your study. Nevertheless, you must design and conduct your proposed study in a manner that precludes having so many limitations that the results derived from it are unusable and impractical.

As you know from your research methods book, research designs that control for (or account for) the various threats to internal and external validity will ensure that your study's results are not only internally valid and reliable but externally generalizable as well. This in turn will keep your study's limitations to a reasonable number.

What's a delimitation? A *delimitation* addresses how your proposed study has to be narrow in scope in an effort to make it practical to implement; that is, your study, by necessity, has to be bounded to some degree—all research studies have delimitations.

Section 9 is also the place to explain the things that you are not going to do and why you have chosen not to do them: the literature you will *not* review (and why), the population you are *not* studying (and why), and the methodological procedures you will *not* use (and why). Your delimitations should be limited to the things that your readers might reasonably expect you to do but that you—for clearly explained reasons—have decided not to do.

Technically, limitations (factors you cannot control) are distinct from delimitations (factors you control). Examples of delimitations might include the following:

1. To ensure the manageability of my data collection plan, my measuring instruments will only use closed-ended response items and will not include open-ended items.

2. Because I will be collecting data through intensive 2-hour client interviews, my sampling frame will contain only those clients who reside in Cook County.

On an overly simplified level, Section 9 of your research proposal is a crude evaluation of how well your Method section was thought out:

(8a) the appropriateness of the research design you selected that will answer your research question (or test your hypothesis)

(8b) the rationale as to how, why, where, and when you selected your sample

(8c) the appropriateness of the kind of measurements you plan to use to measure your variables

(8d) the appropriateness of the sample (data source) you plan to use, and what data collecting methods you chose to use to gather data from your sample

(8e) the appropriateness of your proposed data analysis techniques

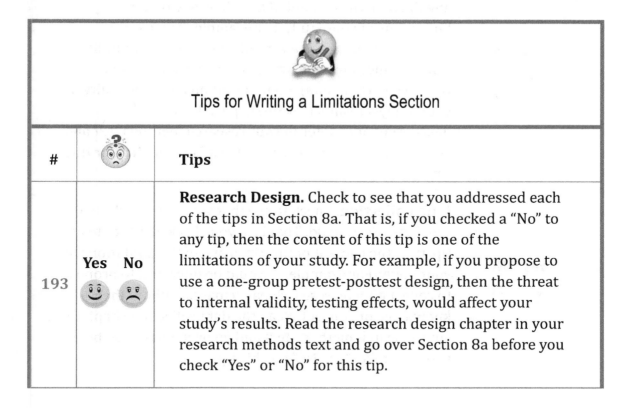

		Tips for Writing a Limitations Section
#		**Tips**
193	**Yes No**	**Research Design.** Check to see that you addressed each of the tips in Section 8a. That is, if you checked a "No" to any tip, then the content of this tip is one of the limitations of your study. For example, if you propose to use a one-group pretest-posttest design, then the threat to internal validity, testing effects, would affect your study's results. Read the research design chapter in your research methods text and go over Section 8a before you check "Yes" or "No" for this tip.

194	**Yes No**	**Sample.** Check to see that you addressed each of the tips in Section 8b. That is, if you checked a "No" to any tip, then the content of this tip is one of the limitations of your study. For example, if you propose to use a random sample of research participants drawn from a specific sampling frame (such as one specific community), then you will not be able to generalize the results of your study to individuals who live outside your sampling frame (or chosen community). Read the sampling chapter in your research methods text and go over Section 8b before you check "Yes" or "No" for this tip.
195	**Yes No**	**Instrumentation.** Check to see that you addressed each of the tips in Section 8c. That is, if you checked a "No" to any tip, then the content of this tip is one of the limitations of your study. For example, if you are proposing to measure a variable with a non-culturally-sensitive measuring instrument (as pertains to your research participants), then the validity and reliability of your study's results may be suspect. Read the measurement chapter in your research methods text and go over Section 8c before you check "Yes" or "No" for this tip.
196	**Yes No**	**Data Collection.** Check to see that you addressed each of the tips in Section 8d. That is, if you checked a "No" to any tip, then the content of this tip is one of the limitations of your study. For example, it would be unethical to propose to collect data on research participants without their knowledge or consent. Read the data collection chapter in your research methods text and go over Section 8d before you check "Yes" or "No" for this tip.

197	**Yes** **No** ☺ ☹	**Data Analysis.** Check to see that you addressed each of the tips in Section 8e. That is, if you checked a "No" to any tip, then the content of this tip is one of the limitations of your study. For example, if you propose to use the wrong data analysis methods to analyze your data, then the results of your study will be suspect, if not outright wrong. Read the data analysis chapter in your research methods text and go over Section 8e before you check "Yes" or "No" for this tip.
198	**Yes** **No** ☺ ☹	Check with your research instructor to see if he/she has any examples of Limitations sections from other research proposals to show you.

BOX 9.1

Example of a Limitations Section from an Article That Appeared in a Professional Journal

Vida Alegre:
Preliminary Findings of a Depression Intervention for Immigrant Latino Mothers[1]

STUDY LIMITATIONS AND DIRECTIONS FOR FUTURE RESEARCH

Although this study demonstrated feasibility—participants exposed to the intervention experienced a sustained reduction in depressive symptoms—limitations presented themselves.

First, the high dropout rate led to a small sample size that limited our ability to control other variables that might contribute to lower levels of depression, such as taking psychotropic medication or seeking out other forms of therapy. In addition, the high drop-out rate suggest that future studies with this population must include a better tracking system for participants, as a subgroup of women would have moved and/or changed her number before the intervention ends.

Second, because the study aimed to establish feasibility, this study does not include a comparison group; therefore, threats to internal validity cannot be dismissed. Therefore, a study with a larger sample and a randomized experimental design is needed to further test the strength of the intervention.

A third limitation rests on the use of bilingual students; the replication of this intervention is limited to communities that can draw upon institutions of higher education within close proximity. For those communities without such institution, training models need to be developed that equip members of the Hispanic community to work as paraprofessionals or peer counselors.

Fourth, despite overcoming a number of obstacles that affect service access—the lack of bilingual providers, the availability of child care, and the lack of culturally tailored services for immigrants—Vida Alegre was unable to overcome the problem of transportation. Although the lack of transportation may negatively bias the effect of the intervention, in a real world sense, transportation remains a formidable obstacle across services sectors.

---

[1]Piedra, L.M., & Byoun, S. (2012). Vida Alegre: Preliminary findings of a depression intervention for immigrant Latino mothers. *Research on Social Work Practice, 22,* 138–150.

BOX 9.2

Example of a Limitations Section from an Article
That Appeared in a Professional Journal

Readiness for College Engagement among Students Who Have Aged Out of Foster Care[1]

LIMITATIONS

The research design for this exploratory study was a one-group cross sectional survey and is thus subject to the usual limitations of such a design. A noteworthy limitation is selection bias with respect to our sample of former foster youth. As discussed earlier, most foster youth do not make it to college. Our sample earned high school GPAs and ACT scores that were necessary to gain admittance to a four-year college. This notable achievement alone suggests the 81 students from foster care in our sample may have perceived themselves as better prepared for college than other foster youth whose academic qualifications limited them to community colleges or other post-secondary educational programs.

Moreover, students in our sample had enrolled in a comprehensive college support program that provided support in the areas of education, finances, housing, health, socialization, identity development, and life skills. However, since they did not begin this program until after completing the CSI, program enrollment could not have affected the students' perceptions, but it is possible that students' expectations of the program may have played a role in their ratings.

Another limitation is that the study measured self-perceptions of readiness for college prior to starting the college experience; therefore, the findings of the study are best understood as a measure of the students' intentions and not their actions: How they *think* they will feel and behave regarding their college coursework based on their high-school experiences and any limited exposure to college life.

---

[1]Unrau, Y.A., Font, S.A., & Rawls, G. (2012). Readiness for college engagement among students who have aged out of foster care. *Children and Youth Services Review, 34*, 76–83.

Homework Assignment 9

Writing Limitations Sections for Research Proposals

Boxes 9.1 and 9.2 present two Limitations sections from two different social work journal articles. Download and read one of the articles. Now that you are familiar with the research study depicted in the article you selected:

In the white space below, write a Limitations section you feel the authors *should have* written for the research proposal their study was based upon. The box will expand as you type.

NOTE: You do not have a copy of the authors' research proposal. You only have a copy of the article that resulted from the implementation of their proposal. Your main objective is to edit, revise, rearrange, and/or modify the authors' published Limitations section as you think it *should have* appeared in their research proposal.

* Use all the tips in this section to write your hypothetical proposal's Limitations section (e.g., did the research design control for confounding variables?).
* Submit your revised Limitations section to your instructor, pointing out all the revisions you made and why you made them.

Your Name(s):
Your Identification Number(s) (if any):
Assignment 9. Title of Selected Article:

Type your revised Limitation section here.
(Box will automatically expand as you type)

Section 9
Writing a Limitations Section for Your Research Proposal

Write a Limitations section for your research proposal in the white space provided below. The box will expand as you type.

- Use all the tips in this section to write your Limitations section.
- If possible, show your Limitations section to your classmates for their feedback.
- Revise your Limitations section based on your classmates' feedback.
- Submit your Limitations section to your instructor for comments.

Your Name(s):

Your Identification Number(s) (if any):

Title of Your Research Proposal:

Type your Limitations section here.
(Box will automatically expand as you type)

SIGNIFICANCE

(1–3 sentences for each important point)

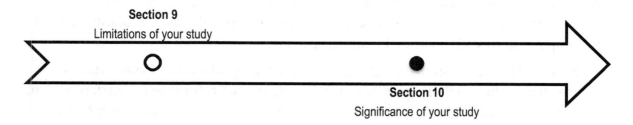

Section 9

Limitations of your study

Section 10

Significance of your study

Evaluating the Proposed Solution

Section 10 is an extremely difficult section to write—especially if you are an undergraduate who may not have a lot of social work practice experience under your belt. Where you are in school determines how significant your study should be to the advancement of civilization and the universe.

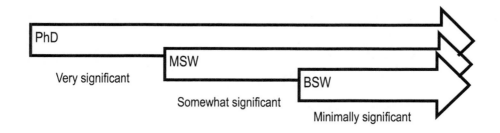

PhD

Very significant

MSW

Somewhat significant

BSW

Minimally significant

Significance of Research Proposals by Social Work Degree

If your research proposal is being completed as a requirement for an undergraduate course, for example, then the overall practical day-to-day significance of your proposed study does not have to be truly astonishing and an effort to save humanity.

In this case, your proposal writing is more of a learning experience than a life-saving event, and you may wish to hold off on saving humanity until you're in graduate school.

On the other hand, if your proposal is being written for a graduate-level course, then your instructor would obviously expect it to be more directly relevant to day-to-day contemporary social work practice than an undergraduate venture. And at the doctoral level, it goes without saying that your proposal must be totally relevant and important to social work education, practice, or policy.

Section 10 forces you to contemplate the overall significance of your study's results; that is, how will the results of your study impact future social work research, theory, day-to-day practice interventions, educational curricula, and policy? Will your study's results refine, revise, or extend existing knowledge in your problem area? Note that such refinements, revisions, or extensions may have substantive, theoretical, or methodological significance.

As you know, your Abstract and Introduction sections contained subsections when it comes to the "significance" of your study. In a nutshell, Section 10 is just an extensive elaboration of those two subsections.

Tips for Writing a Significance Section

#		Tips
199	Yes No	Check to see that you have discussed what the results of your study will mean to the theoretical framework that framed your study.
200	Yes No	Check to see that you have provided various suggestions that subsequent research studies may focus upon given the projected findings of your study.
201	Yes No	Check to see that you have provided concrete suggestions how the results of your study could affect social work educators, practitioner, and policy makers (if appropriate).
202	Yes No	Check to see that you have provided concrete suggestions on how the results of your study could affect social work programs and agencies (if appropriate).
203	Yes No	Check to see that you have made suggestions as what is to be improved or changed as a result of your proposed research study.
204	Yes No	Check with your research instructor to see if he/she has any examples of significance sections from other research proposals to show you.

BOX 10.1

Example of a Significance for Future Research Section from an
Article That Appeared in a Professional Journal

Readiness for College Engagement among Students
Who Have Aged Out of Foster Care[1]

RESEARCH IMPLICATIONS

This study adds to the literature by highlighting foster youths' readiness to engage
in college and comparing their readiness to the general population of freshman
FTIAC students. With the proliferation of campus-based programs supporting
students from foster care on two- and four-year college campuses, researchers will
have more opportunities to study this uniquely vulnerable and under-served
population.

It is important that future research include variables to measure the foster-
care experience itself, since foster youth can vary on many factors such as age of
entry into the foster care system, number and type of foster care placements they
have received, and level of support from the foster family after their cases are
closed. The variation in childhood histories and foster care experiences likely
influence the degree of academic motivation, social motivation, receptivity to
services, and coping among former foster-care youth in the young adult years.

Foster-care research strongly suggests that the aspirations of foster youth do
not match up to their behaviors or actions; that is, intentions do not automatically
translate into actions. And, since this study measured perception and not action,
further studies of a longitudinal nature are needed to determine if students from
foster care are more or less likely to actually utilize campus-based services and
support compared to their non-foster-care student peers.

Including a wider range of psychological variables and their effects on the
coping strategies of students from foster care would also increase understanding
of how best to assist these students when obstacles that interfere with academic
progress arise.

––––––––

[1]Unrau, Y.A., Font, S.A., & Rawls, G. (2012). Readiness for college engagement among
students who have aged out of foster care. *Children and Youth Services Review, 34*, 76–83.

BOX 10.2

Example of a Significance for Social Work Practice Section from an Article That Appeared in a Professional Journal

Readiness for College Engagement among Students Who Have Aged Out of Foster Care[1]

PRACTICE IMPLICATIONS

The findings of this study shed light on how child welfare and education professionals can address the needs of students from foster care. Past research studies have strongly made the case that students from foster care have a high risk of dropping out of college. Lack of family privilege, the premature launch into independence, financial difficulties, housing instability, and lack of access to health care are among the significant barriers that students from foster care must tackle above and beyond the normal stresses of college life.

Educating child welfare and college professionals about the unique educational obstacles faced by students from foster care as well as their higher-than-average levels of academic and social motivation and openness to academic and counseling services can give these professionals a better perspective on how to engage this unique student group. Early engagement with foster youth in college is critical since foster youth may possess greater confidence than competence to engage in the college environment.

The Appendix provides a selective list of policy and practice resources prepared by Casey Family Programs that can inform professionals about the needs of, and the supports and programs for, students from foster care who are often a hidden and fragmented population on college campuses. Professionals working in ways to support college students from foster care must be skillful in engaging students and eliciting relevant information to perform the job of assisting students in need. Casey Family Programs has developed recommendations for financial-aid staff about sensitive approaches to communication with students from foster care and unaccompanied homeless youth.

For example, they suggest that students from foster care find it helpful when college staff professionals conduct conversations that include asking personal questions in environments where they cannot be overheard; take time to explain questions and make sure students understand the answers before ending the interaction; walk students through next steps (e.g., completion of a form, escort to next department and introduce them to someone before leaving); and follow up with students via e-mail, text, or phone to ensure they completed all steps.

---

[1]Unrau, Y.A., Font, S.A., & Rawls, G. (2012). Readiness for college engagement among students who have aged out of foster care. *Children and Youth Services Review, 34*, 76–83.

   **Homework Assignment 10**

Writing Significance Sections for Research Proposals

Boxes 10.1 and 10.2 present one Significance section from a social work journal article. The authors divided the section into two parts: (Research Implications and Practice Implications). Download and read the article. Now that you are familiar with the research study depicted in the article:

In the white space below, write one Significance section with two subsections (one for research and the other for practice) you feel the authors *should have* written for the research proposal. The box will expand as you type. Your main objective is to edit, revise, rearrange, and/or modify the authors' Significance section in an effort to make it clearer, more concise, and easier to read and follow.

• Use all the tips in this section to rewrite your Significance section (e.g., is each instrument referred to in the appendix?).

• Submit your revised Significance section to your instructor, pointing out all the revisions you made and why you made them.

Your Name(s):
Your Identification Number(s) (if any):
Assignment 10

Type your revised Significance section here.
(Box will automatically expand as you type)

Section 10
Writing a Significance Section for Your Research Proposal

Write a Significance section for your research proposal in the white space provided below. The box will expand as you type.

- Use all the tips in this section to write your Significance section.
- If possible, show your Significance section to your classmates for their feedback.
- Revise your Significance section based on your classmates' feedback.
- Submit your Significance section to your instructor for comments.

Your Name(s):

Your Identification Number(s) (if any):

Title of Your Research Proposal:

Type your Significance section here.
(Box will automatically expand as you type)

PART VI
Back Matter

The back matter of a research proposal includes two sections: Section 11 contains the references you cited throughout your proposal, and Section 12 comprises all your appendixes. Unfortunately, most naïve proposal writers neglect the back matter of their proposals. This is a serious mistake because the people who review research proposals for potential funding pay particular attention to how these two sections are completed—especially Section 12, which contains your appendixes.

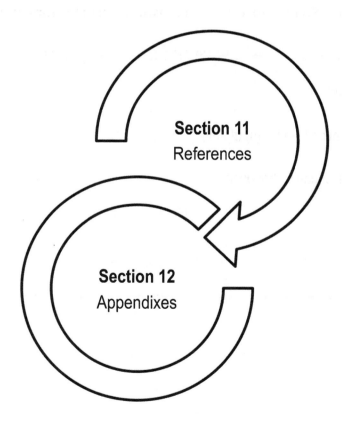

Section 11
References

Section 12
Appendixes

REFERENCES

(As many as needed)

Section 11
References cited within the proposal

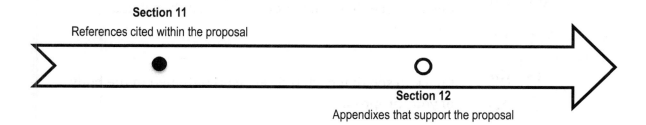

Section 12
Appendixes that support the proposal

Back Matter

Section 11 is only a list of your references. We assume you know how to format your references in APA style. You can use this book as a guide to how they are formatted if your memory needs a bit of refreshing..

#		Tips
	Tips for Writing a References Section	
205	Yes No	Check to see that you really understand how to reference material for your papers. If not, obtain one of the many inexpensive books that can be found on Amazon.com that deal with the subject.

206	**Yes** **No**	Check to see that each and every reference in this section is 100% complete and accurate.
207	**Yes** **No**	Check to see that all of your references are formatted to APA specifications.
208	**Yes** **No**	Check to see that your references are alphabetized correctly.
209	**Yes** **No**	Check to see that each reference is contained in the body of your proposal.
210	**Yes** **No**	Check to see that only the references cited in your proposal are included in your reference list.
211	**Yes** **No**	Check with your research instructor to see if he/she has any examples of References sections from other research proposals to show you.

APPENDIXES

(As many as needed)

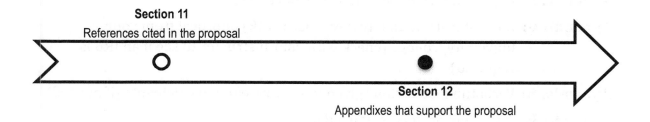

Section 11
References cited in the proposal

Section 12
Appendixes that support the proposal

Back Matter

Appendixes are absolutely essential to include in your research proposal. They can easily make or break your proposal. They should be devoted to those aspects of your project that are of secondary interest to your readers. In short, appendixes are used for the material that can't be included in the body of the paper due to space limitations.

First, assume that many of your readers will only have a short amount of time to read your proposal, will only read its main body, and will skip the appendixes. Second, assume that some of your readers *will* want additional information that is not found in the body of your proposal—that is the purpose of the appendixes.

It is more than likely that you won't use all the appendixes we have included in this section. These appendixes are required no matter what kind of study you propose: C, D, G, J, K, L, M, N, and O. However, if you are not proposing to do your study within a social work agency, you will not need Appendixes A and B. Likewise, if you are not going to use human research participants in your study, you won't include Appendixes E, F, H, and I.

Appendix A: Copies of official letters of permission to conduct your research study in a social work agency or program (if needed)

Appendix B: Cooperating agency description (if needed)

Appendix C: Time lines

Appendix D: Measuring instruments (an individual appendix for each instrument)

Appendix E: Copy of informed consent form (if needed)

Appendix F: Copy of informed assent form (if needed)

Appendix G: Copy of institutional review board (IRB) approval from your university/college (check with your instructor to see if an IRB is required)

Appendix H: Verbatim instructions given to your research participants (if needed)

Appendix I: Interview protocols (if needed)

Appendix J: Data collection plan

Appendix K: Data analysis plan

Appendix L: Personnel (if needed)

Appendix M: Copies of resumes of key people

Appendix N: Dissemination plan

Appendix O: Budget

APPENDIX A

(Permission to do your study, if applicable)

Appendix A is the place to include letters from an agency's Executive Director who has provided permission for you to implement your proposal within the agency. Your study would more than likely use some of the agency's resources and clientele. It is very important that the person who signs the letter of permission actually knows what your study is all about. There should be no surprises when you show up at the door.

In a nutshell, make sure the agency's Executive Director has thoroughly read your research proposal and understands exactly *what* you are going to do, *why* you are going to do it, *who* are you going to do it to, *how* you are going to do it, *when* you are going to do it, *where* are you going to do it, and more importantly, *how* are you obtaining informed consent and/or assent for your research participants—who just happen to be the clientele of the agency.

Appendix A is not needed if you don't require any letters of support to do your study. Please note that Appendix A is not the place for the Institutional Review Board (IRB) approval letters; those are contained in Appendix G. You will need a support letter from an agency's Executive Director to include in your proposal that you submit to your university/college's IRB.

Box A is an actual example of how an agency's Executive Director wrote a letter of support and at the same time provided permission for researchers to do a research study within his agency and use the agency's clientele as research participants.

Funding agencies would like to know that others (besides yourself) feel strongly enough about your proposed project that they are willing to write a letter of support. The more support letters the better. Do not write a support letter for the agency's Executive Director to sign. Have the Executive Director write it.

The support letter must be substantive in nature and addressed to the funding agency and not to "To Whom It May Concern." This dreaded phrase makes it appear that you are applying to many different potential funding agencies and the Executive Director is using the same letter for each. In reality this may be the case, however, so make sure the Executive Director personalizes each letter to the specific potential funding agency.

BOX A

Example of a Support Letter for a Research Study to Take Place within a Social Work Agency

Chatham-Kent Children's Services (CKCS) Help-Seeking Project for Adolescents in Out-of-Home Placement: A Research Proposal[1]

Dear Ms. Funder:

We are pleased to provide you with the attached research proposal as a response to your "Request for Proposals."

We are a large, integrated, multiservice agency that serves the protection, mental health, and developmental needs of the children and youth in our community. In addition, we have the mandate to deliver prevention and community services for children and their families.

We are glad to once again have the collaboration of Drs. Grinnell and Unrau from the School of Social Work at Western Michigan University in Kalamazoo, Michigan. I personally have had the opportunity to previously collaborate with both Drs. Grinnell and Unrau on a wide range of child welfare–related topics. You will note from our attached vitas that we have collaborated on child sexual abuse, in-home support, and related program evaluation issues.

Over the years, and as a team, I believe we have developed relevant and useable practice findings. The research topic is not only timely but we should be able to put the results to good use to improve the lives of youth in our care and better prepare them for independence.

If you have any questions whatsoever please don't hesitate to contact me.

Mike Stephens, MSW
Chief Executive Officer

APPENDIX B

(Cooperating agency description, if applicable)

If you will be working with a social work agency, it is a good idea to provide a detailed description of what it does in Appendix B. All you need to do is provide the six pieces of information below on one sheet of paper:

1. Name of the agency
2. Complete address of the agency
3. General telephone number of the agency
4. Brief description of the major services the agency provides
5. Specific persons within the agency that you will be working with along with each one's telephone number and/or extension
6. Description of what the role of each person will be in reference to your research study; that is, what will each person specifically be responsible for?

If you will be working with more than one agency, you will need to prepare a single-page description for each one that follows the same format. Remember, one page for each agency.

Appendix B is also a good place to put a copy of a letter written by the agency's Executive Director (or similar person) that specifies how the agency plans on using the results of your study (if appropriate, of course).

Box B is an example of how an agency plans to implement the results of a research study into its day-to-day practices if the proposal is funded and how the results of the study will benefit the social service delivery system within the agency.

BOX B

Example of a Support Letter That Addresses How the Agency Will Use the Results from a Research Study

Chatham-Kent Children's Services (CKCS) Help-Seeking Project for Adolescents in Out-of-Home Placement: A Research Proposal[1]

Dear Ms. Funder,

Please find enclosed 10 copies of our "Phase 2" grant proposal that we wish to submit to your organization for funding: "Chatham-Kent Children's Services Help-Seeking Project for Adolescents in Out-of-Home Placement." Our proposal is a direct result of the $10,000 Grants in Aid funds we received from your organization last year.

We're really excited about our project. In fact, if our intervention is shown to be successful, we will implement it in our day-to-day practice activities via reorganizing our service delivery structure. Since we initially received your "Phase 1" funding, we, along with the two researchers from WMU, have been thinking through various in-house strategies toward sustaining the intervention without extra funding from outside sources.

If you have any questions, please do not hesitate to contact me at your earliest convenience.

I look forward to hearing from you, and thank you for your time.

Sincerely,

Mike Stephens, MSW
Chief Executive Officer

---

[1]Unrau, Y., & Grinnell, R.M., Jr. (2005). *Chatham-Kent Children's Services (CKCS) Help-Seeking Project for Adolescents in Out-of-Home Placement: A Research Proposal.* Submitted to Provincial Centre of Excellence for Child and Youth Mental Health at CHEO. Ottawa, Ontario, Canada K1H 8L1.

APPENDIX C

(Time lines)

As you know, Appendixes A and B are optional because they will not be relevant if your study is not going to use a social work agency. Appendix C, however, is not optional—it's required as it outlines your proposed work schedule, outlining the various activities you will be doing with specific time lines for each activity.

It is important that you present accurate, realistic time lines that allocate an adequate amount of time for all the different activities you will perform in your proposed project. Don't forget to include time for revising, revising, revising, editing, editing, editing, and producing the final product.

More often than not, most social work students seriously underestimate the amount of time it will take them to conduct the research and write the final research reports (manuscripts) that are based on their research proposals. Thus, you need to make a best guesstimate time line that outlines the amount of time it will take for each of your activities—from your literature review to the final submission of your manuscript for possible publication.

The example here is a crude sample time line submitted by one student. Keep in mind that time lines can vary dramatically, depending on the circumstances of the research endeavor. In this case, the student is preparing a preliminary literature review for the proposal and will need to complete it by the time the study is actually over. Other students may compile the complete literature review while preparing their proposals. Also, this student was employed full-time and could devote only evenings and weekends to carrying out the research study (Patten, 2010).

1. Complete literature review from my research proposal. (1 month)
2. Have completed literature review assessed by my instructor. (2 weeks)
3. Obtain mailing lists of research participants from the Department of Social Services. (2 weeks)

4. Prepare survey cover letter and first draft of questionnaire. (1 week)

5. Have cover letter and questionnaire reviewed by my instructor. (1 week)

6. Pilot test cover letter and questionnaire. (3 weeks)

7. Revise cover letter and questionnaire based on feedback from pilot test. (2 weeks)

8. Have revised cover letter and questionnaire reviewed by my instructor. (2 weeks)

9. Obtain approval from my university's institutional review board. (3 weeks)

10. Write the Method section of the final research report. (2 weeks)

11. Have the Method section reviewed by my instructor. (2 weeks)

12. Mail letter and questionnaire to sample, and wait for responses. (3 weeks)

13. Mail follow-up questionnaire and wait for responses. (2 weeks)

14. Tabulate responses. Conduct descriptive and inferential analyses. (3 weeks)

15. Write the Findings section of the final research report. (2 weeks)

16. Have the Findings sections reviewed by my instructor. (2 weeks)

17. Assemble the first draft of the complete report. Have it reviewed by my instructor and at the University Writing Center for mechanical flaws in grammar, punctuation, etc. (2 weeks)

18. Submit the complete first draft (revised in light of previous step) to my instructor for initial review. (2 weeks)

19. Rewrite and revise in light of the previous step, and resubmit for feedback. (2 weeks)

20. Make final changes based on previous step; format the final report and submit it to a social work journal for possible publication. (4 weeks)

———————

REFERENCE

Patten, M.L. (2010). *Understanding research methods: An overview of the essentials* (7th ed.). Glendale, CA: Pryczak.

APPENDIX D

(Measuring instruments)

ATTACHING STANDARDIZED MEASURING INSTRUMENTS

Appendix D starts the appendixes that contain good, clear copies of your standardized measuring instruments *along with* their appropriate scoring instructions. There must be a separate appendix for each measuring instrument (and the instructions on how to complete them) that you plan to use. Or, to put it another way, one instrument for each variable you plan to measure—simple as that.

Thus, if you have five variables, you will have an appropriate measuring instrument for each, and five separate appendixes: D_1, D_2, D_3, D_4, and D_5.

Figure D_1 contains an example of a standardized measuring instrument that measures self-esteem, and Figure D_2 contains basic information about the instrument.

If a measuring instrument is copyrighted, you need to state that you will obtain official written permission from the copyright holder to reproduce the instrument for your study *before* you actually begin to implement your study.

As you know, you will be referring to each measuring instrument (and thus each individual appendix) in your Research Design section (8a), Sampling section (8b), Instrumentation section (8c), Data Collection section (8d), and Data Analysis section (8e).

ATTACHING YOUR OWN HOMEGROWN INSTRUMENTS

If you are creating your own instrument(s), include a draft copy of the actual measuring instrument you plan to use, such as a survey, questionnaire, or interview schedule. This will let your reviewers know that you're serious about your proposed project. Put "DRAFT" at the top of each homegrown measuring instrument, and make them look as much like the final product as possible.

If you will be using interviews as your data collection method, include a draft copy of the specific questions that you plan to use. Remember, the questions you ask and the answers you receive must be directly relevant to your research question (or hypothesis).

Under no circumstances should you dump copies of all of your measuring instruments into one appendix in a sloppy manner. It will not impress your reviewers the least bit.

Figure D_1 illustrates how a measuring instrument needs to be displayed, and Figure D_2 (Continued) demonstrates the material that should accompany the instrument.

Name:_____ Today's Date:_____

This questionnaire is designed to measure how you see yourself. It is not a test, so there are no right or wrong answers. Please answer each item as carefully and as accurately as you can by placing a number beside each one as follows:

1 = None of the time
2 = Very rarely
3 = A little of the time
4 = Some of the time
5 = A good part of the time
6 = Most of the time
7 = All of the time

1. ___ I feel that people would not like me if they really knew me well.
2. ___ I feel that others get along much better than I do.
3. ___ I feel that I am a beautiful person.
4. ___ When I am with others I feel they are glad I am with them.
5. ___ I feel that people really like to talk with me.
6. ___ I feel that I am a very competent person.
7. ___ I think I make a good impression on others.
8. ___ I feel that I need more self-confidence.
9. ___ When I am with strangers I am very nervous.
10. ___ I think that I am a dull person.
11. ___ I feel ugly.
12. ___ I feel that others have more fun than I do.
13. ___ I feel that I bore people.
14. ___ I think my friends find me interesting.
15. ___ I think I have a good sense of humor.
16. ___ I feel very self-conscious when I am with strangers.
17. ___ I feel that if I could be more like other people I would have it made.
18. ___ I feel that people have a good time when they are with me.
19. ___ I feel like a wallflower when I go out.
20. ___ I feel I get pushed around more than others.
21. ___ I think I am a rather nice person.
22. ___ I feel that people really like me very much.
23. ___ I feel that I am a likeable person.
24. ___ I am afraid I will appear foolish to others.
25. ___ My friends think very highly of me.

_____

3, 4, 5, 6, 7, 14, 15, 18, 21, 22, 23, 25

Figure D₁
Hudson's *Index of Self-Esteem*

AUTHOR: Walter W. Hudson

PURPOSE: To measure problems with self-esteem.

DESCRIPTION: The *ISE* is a 25-item scale designed to measure the degree, severity, or magnitude of a problem the client has with self-esteem. Self-esteem is considered as the evaluative component of self-concept. The *ISE* is written in very simple language, is easily administered, and easily scored. Because problems with self-esteem are often central to social and psychological difficulties, this instrument has a wide range of utility for a number of clinical problems.

   The *ISE* has a cutting score of 30 (+ or – 5), with scores above 30 indicating the respondent has a clinically significant problem and scores below 30 indicating the individual has no such problem. Another advantage of the *ISE* is that it is one of nine scales of the *Clinical Measurement Package* (Hudson, 1982), all of which are administered and scored the same way.

NORMS: This scale was derived from tests of 1,745 respondents, including single and married individuals, clinical and nonclinical populations, college students, and nonstudents. Respondents included Caucasians, Japanese, and Chinese Americans, and a smaller number of members of other ethnic groups. Not recommended for use with children under the age of 12.

SCORING: For a detailed description on how to score the *ISE,* see: www.walmyr.com.

RELIABILITY: The *ISE* has a mean alpha of .93, indicating excellent internal consistency, and an excellent (low) S.E.M. of 3.70. The *ISE* also has excellent stability with a two-hour test-retest correlation of .92.

VALIDITY: The *ISE* has good know-groups validity, significantly distinguishing between clients judged by clinicians to have problems in the area of self-esteem and those known not to. Further, the *ISE* has very good construct validity, correlating well with a range of other measures with which it should correlate highly, e.g., depression, happiness, sense of identity, and scores on the *Generalized Contentment Scale* (depression).

PRIMARY REFERENCE: Hudson, W.W. (1982). *The clinical measurement package: A field manual.* Chicago: Dorsey.

Figure D₁ (Continued)
Basic Information about Hudson's *Index of Self-Esteem*

APPENDIX E

(Informed consent form, if applicable)

First and foremost, reread the research ethics chapter in your research methods text before you write a consent form. As you know from Section 8a (on research design), Section 8b (on sampling), Section 8c (on instrumentation), Section 8d (on data collection), and Section 8e (on data analysis), ethical issues arise when you want to use research participants in your proposed study. You always need to address possible ethical issues in your proposal when you use humans as data sources.

First and foremost, you must plan to protect your participants' privacy. By collecting your research participants' anonymous responses to mailed questionnaires and surveys, for example, you provide them with this much-needed protection. If you will be providing anonymity, you should state that in your proposal. Remember that anonymity means you do not know who answered what on a particular measuring instrument.

You need to consider how to shield your research participants from psychological harm as you design your study (e.g., experimental or control groups), select your research participants and measuring instruments, and decide on your data collection and analysis plans. This all boils down to writing a consent form that your research participants need to sign.

A written consent form should be only part of the process of informing your research participants of their roles and rights as volunteers in your purposed study. It must give potential participants a basic description of the purpose of your study, the study's procedures, and their rights as voluntary participants. All information must be provided in plain and simple language:

- that participants are being asked to participate in a research study
- the names of the investigators and their affiliations
- the purposes of the research, simply explained

- the study's procedures

- the expected duration of participation

- any reasonably foreseeable risks or discomforts

- any safeguards to minimize the risks

- any benefits to the participant or to others that may reasonably be expected from the research study. (In most cases, the study is not being performed for the benefit of the participants but for the potential benefit of others. This broader social benefit to the public should be made explicit.)

- in cases where an incentive is offered, a description of the incentive and of how and under what conditions it is to be obtained

- appropriate alternative procedures or courses of treatment, if applicable

- the extent, if any, to which confidentiality of records identifying the participant will be maintained (not an issue unless participants can be identified)

- any restrictions on confidentiality. (For instance, if any of the information gained during the study might have to be disclosed as required by law, as in instances of child abuse, absolute confidentiality cannot be assured.)

- what monetary compensation or medical or psychological treatment will be provided for any research-related injury (if more than minimal risk)

- contact information for questions about the study (name, office address, and phone contacts for the researcher, faculty advisor, and IRB staff). Do not include home phone numbers.

- that participation is voluntary, and that the participant may discontinue participation at any time without penalty or loss of benefits to which he or she is otherwise entitled (e.g., in their standing as a patient, student, employee, and so forth)

- that the researcher will keep one copy of the signed consent form and give another signed copy to the participant

Most universities/colleges, and most large social service agencies for that matter, require that all research proposals be reviewed by their internal committees, which will consider all these issues. These committees are likely to pay special attention to what you will be measuring and how you will be measuring it, with an eye to whether participants are adequately protected. These committees will also be reviewing your informed-consent form, so you should obtain a copy of your institution's guidelines on preparing such a form early in the development of your proposal.

More than likely, your university/college will have examples of consent forms that can be found in their research offices or some other similar department. Many times universities/colleges have online templates you can use as guides.

In any event, if you are going to use human research participants in your study, you will probably have to submit your proposal to your university/college's institutional review board (IRB) for their approval before you start collecting data. You can easily get an expedited student review if your study is simple, straightforward, and doesn't involve assigning individuals to groups or collecting data through interviews. Your instructor would be the person in the know when it comes to helping you get your research proposal through the incredible maze of the university/college IRB.

Obviously, you do not have to submit your research proposal to your IRB if you do not plan on implementing your study.

BOX E

Example of a Consent Form from a Research Proposal

Chatham-Kent Children's Services (CKCS) Help-Seeking Project for Adolescents in Out-of-Home Placement: A Research Proposal[1]

You are invited to have your clients participate in Chatham-Kent Children's Services (CKCS) Help-Seeking Project for Adolescents in Out-of-Home Placement. The project is funded by the Provincial Centre of Excellence for Child and Youth Mental Health. The primary person in charge of the project is Mike Stephens, Chief Executive Officer of CKCS.

This handout describes our project and will help you decide if you want to have your clients participate. You are 100% free to choose whether or not you will have your clients take part in the study. Before you decide, however, you need to know what will be expected of them if you agree to have them participate and the risks and benefits of their participation. Please take time to read this handout.

There are no negative consequences for either you or your clients in reference to your decision as to their potential participation. Your clients can drop out of the study at any time. The services they receive from CKCS will not be affected by your decision to have them participate in this project.

If you agree to have your clients take part in the project they will be asked to sign a separate assent form. The assent form is a shorter version of this consent form and contains important information about the project. When they sign the assent form, they give their "consent," which means that they agree to participate in the project.

WHAT'S THE PROJECT ABOUT ANYWAY?

The main purpose of our project is to find out whether a workshop on help-seeking for youth living in out-of-home placement at CKCS will help them become more skilled at asking for help when personal or emotional problems arise. We don't yet know if our help-seeking workshop works. So we have designed a project that will involve about 120 youth, ages 12 years and older, who are living at CKCS.

Half of the youth who participate in the project will attend a special workshop, and the other half will not. The workshop will give them information and ideas about how to seek help when personal or emotional problems arise. We will then compare the help-seeking skills of those youth who attended the workshop with those who did not in order to learn whether the workshop was helpful. They will be assigned, by chance, to a group who attend the workshop, or to a group who do not attend. That is, they may or may not attend the workshop even though they agree to participate in the project (via an assent form).

If we learn that the workshop is helpful in the way we expect, then all youth who did not get to attend the workshop will be offered a chance to attend it at a later date, as long as they are still living at CKCS.

In total, about 120 youth will participate in the project. Everyone will be asked to complete a set of questionnaires at four different times: this week, 5 weeks from now, 10 weeks from now, and 5 months from now. Step by step, this is what will happen if you agree to have your clients participate in the project AND they have also agreed.

1. They will be contacted twice by telephone. Sometime this week, and then again 5 months from now, a CKCS staff member will call them by telephone and ask them questions. The phone interview takes about 30 minutes and includes questions about common emotional and behavioral problems experienced by teenagers. They do not have to answer any questions they don't want to.

2. They will be asked to come to CKCS four times over the next 5 months and to complete four other surveys. These surveys are completed at the CKCS computer lab using a special computer program. Sitting at their own computers and wearing headphones, they will see each question appear on the computer screen and hear the question being read through the headphones.

3. They will answer the questions by clicking the computer mouse. The computer surveys should take about 30 to 40 minutes to complete each time. As we said above, they do not have to answer any questions that they don't want to. They will be paid for their participation. They will receive $10 the first time they answer the survey questions, $15 the second time, $20 the third time, and $30 the fourth time.

4. Snacks also will be provided at each meeting, and bus fare to CKCS will be available if they need it. In addition to the above surveys, a project staff member will review their CKCS case files for information such as their placements, services they have received, and family contacts.

5. By chance, half of the youth participating in the project will be invited to attend a 2- to 3-hour workshop that will include six youths at a time. The workshop will take place at CKCS and be run by a CKCS staff member. The purpose of the workshop is to give them additional information about how they can best get help for their personal or emotional problems while living in a CKCS placement.

UNDER WHAT CIRCUMSTANCES WOULD CKCS END THEIR PARTICIPATION?

If they leave CKCS within 5 weeks of the start of the project, their participation in the project will automatically end.

HOW WILL THEIR PRIVACY BE PROTECTED?

Confidentiality describes what we do to keep information gathered about your clients completely private. In order to protect their privacy in this project:

1. We use numbers instead of names (or other identifiers) on all of the data we obtain so that no one can connect the data with you or them.

2. The data collected for this project will be sent to researchers at Western Michigan University. Once again, the data will not include anything that would individually identify you or them. The researchers and their staff have been trained in protecting everyone's confidentiality.

3. No CKCS staff member will have access to the data that your clients provide as part of this project. All data collected from your clients will not be shared with you (their Children's Service Worker and legal guardian), their foster parents or caregivers, or any other workers at CKCS. The data collected will only be used for this project.

4. All data will be stored in a safe, locked area. The computers for this project are protected by a firewall system, and all users are required to use passwords.

5. All of the adolescents' answers will be kept absolutely private unless a staff member thinks they might be in danger of hurting themselves. For example, if an adolescent tells us that he or she is using illegal drugs, or is thinking of harming him or herself or someone else, project staff are obligated to inform you since you are his or her legal guardian and CKCS Children's Service Worker.

6. The information from the project will be used to write papers, make presentations, and work with other education or research centers to improve out-of-home services for youth. Please remember that their names, or any information that could identify them, will never be used. We will evaluate the survey answers "as a group" and not for any one individual. They will not be identified (for example, by name or social security number) in any reports or publications of this project.

WILL WE SHARE INFORMATION WITH OTHERS?

Yes. As we have said before, if we know or think we know that one of your clients is being abused, under law we must take action to protect that person. We also must report if we hear that they intend to harm themselves or someone else. We will inform you immediately if this is the case.

WHAT ARE THEIR RIGHTS AS A PARTICIPANT IN OUR PROJECT?

As participants in our project, your clients have certain rights that protect them from potential harm. After you, as their legal guardian, have provided your consent to have them participate in the project (via signing this form), their specific rights are as follows:

1. It is up to them to decide if they want to be in our project. That means their participation is completely voluntary.

2. They have the right to change their minds at any time about being in the project. If they decide to leave the project, there will be no penalty of any kind.

3. They have the right to refuse to answer any question(s). Some questions might be personal or sensitive to them. These questions are important to our project and we would like them to answer the questions honestly. However, if there are questions they do not want to answer, they may skip them and move on to other questions.

4. They will be given copies of this Project Description (your consent form). If they want to participate in our project, they will also sign an Assent Form.

5. Their assent forms will also be explained verbally to them. If they have any difficulty in reading these forms, a staff person will read it to them.

6. At any time they can ask any staff member questions about our project. They may also call collect Mike Stephens (x-xxx-xxx-xxxx, extension xxx).

7. If they would like to contact someone outside the project staff with questions or concerns, they can Yvonne Unrau at xxx-xxx-xxxx or Rick Grinnell at xxx-xxx-xxxx, who are the two Western Michigan University researchers involved with the project. They may also contact the Chair, Human Subjects Institutional Review Board (xxx-xxx-xxxx) or the Vice President for Research (xxx-xxx-xxxx) at Western Michigan University if questions or problems arise during the course of the study. They may call collect.

RISKS ASSOCIATED WITH PARTICIPATING IN OUR PROJECT

There are very few risks in this project. The adolescents may, however, feel a little embarrassed or uncomfortable because of the personal nature of some questions on the surveys or due to certain project activities such as role plays in the workshop. Remember, they do not have to answer any questions or take part in any activities at any time.

WHAT ARE THE BENEFITS TO THEM?

Many people find it helpful to think and talk about personal information about themselves and their families. Being in the project gives them a chance to do this. The project may improve our knowledge about how youth in care can better seek help when they need it.

The information gained may help us understand more about how parents, foster parents, and CKCS can work together to help teenagers who are placed in foster or group care.

This information might be used to prevent problems for teenagers in the future and to help those that are having trouble.

As a participant, they will be part of a valuable project that might help other people in the future. Please sign below to show that you have reviewed this Project Description, you consent to have your clients participate, and that you have had all your questions answered.

_____

Social worker's signature (as legal guardian)

_____

Date

Names of your clients who you agree can participate in the project:

_____

_____

_____

_____

———————

[1]Unrau, Y., & Grinnell, R.M., Jr. (2005). *Chatham-Kent Children's Services (CKCS) Help-Seeking Project for Adolescents in Out-of-Home Placement: A Research Proposal.* Submitted to Provincial Centre of Excellence for Child and Youth Mental Health at CHEO. Ottawa, Ontario, Canada K1H 8L1.

APPENDIX F

(Informed assent form, if applicable)

First and foremost, reread the research ethics chapter in your research methods text before you write an assent form. The procedures for obtaining informed assent are similar to those for obtaining informed consent. You should note, however, that an institutional review board (IRB) looks fastidiously at research proposals that require informed assent forms from prospective research participants.

When your proposed study involves populations where informed assent forms are required, plan on the IRB process taking a month or two. If your proposed study plans on using research settings such as schools, residential institutions, departments of human services, or nursing homes, then add another month onto the IRB process. Never underestimate the length of time it takes to get a research proposal through the IRB process when you plan to use vulnerable populations as research participants.

Box F contains an example of an assent form from a research proposal. This assent form was signed by the underage youths after their social workers (their legal guardians) gave their consent for them to participate. It should be noted that the youths could refuse to participate in the study regardless of their social workers' consent. So this study had to have the social workers' consent and their clients' assent.

BOX F

Example of an Assent Form from a Research Proposal

Chatham-Kent Children's Services (CKCS) Help-Seeking Project for Adolescents in Out-of-Home Placement: A Research Proposal[1]

I have been invited to be part of a study entitled "Chatham-Kent Children's Services (CKCS) Help-Seeking Project for Adolescents in Out-of-Home Placement."

The main purpose of the study is to see if a workshop and additional support given to youth living at CKCS will make youth more skilled at asking for help with personal or emotional problems. In this study:

1. I will be phoned by a CKCS staff member twice over 20 weeks and be asked to answer questions on the phone. This will take about 15 minutes each time.

2. I will be invited to come to CKCS four times over the next 20 weeks to answer questions from four other survey questionnaires about my help-seeking behaviors using a special computer program at CKCS.

3. After the first testing, CKCS will pay me $10 (or equivalent).

4. After the second testing point, CKCS will pay me $15 (or equivalent).

5. After the third testing point, CKCS will pay me $20 (or equivalent).

6. After the fourth (and final) time, CKCS will pay me $30 (or equivalent).

7. CKCS will provide food snacks at each testing time.

8. A project staff member will look at my case file to obtain basic information about me such as my age, sex, time in care, etc.

9. My name will not be recorded; instead of recording my name, a number code will be used.

10. I also may be invited to participate in a 2- to 3-hour workshop with a small group of about five other youth in care. The workshop will take place at CKCS and will be run by a CKCS mental health worker and possibly someone who formerly lived in an out-of-home placement.

11. At the workshop, I will get information and ideas about asking for help related to personal or emotional problems that are common with teenagers.

12. If I don't want to participate at this time, the service I receive from CKCS will not be affected.

13. Even if I agree today to participate by signing this form, I can change my mind at any time and withdraw from the study, and there will be no effect on the service I receive from CKCS.

14. If I choose to complete any or all of the questionnaires for the study, then my scores will be sent to researchers at Western Michigan University in Kalamazoo, Michigan.

15. As mentioned previously, my name will not be on any of the surveys that are sent to Michigan. The researchers will use a code number instead of my name. The researchers will keep a list of names and code numbers that will be destroyed once the researchers have looked at all of the questionnaires.

16. All of my answers will be kept private, which means even my Children's Service Worker or caregivers won't know what I say unless project staff members think I might be in danger of hurting myself or others. Then project staff will need to tell my Children's Service Worker.

17. Your signature below indicates that you agree to be interviewed by phone and surveyed on the computer.

YOUR SIGNATURE ALSO INDICATES THAT YOU AGREE:

1. To have your case file at CKCS reviewed for information it contains.

2. To be assigned to participate in a special help-seeking workshop for this project if selected.

3. To allow CKCS to give the researchers your survey results and case file information (your name will not be sent to the researchers).

4. That you have had a chance to ask any questions you may have.

_____

Print your name on above line.

_____ (Date: _____)

Sign your name on the above line and put in today's date.

Assent obtained by: _____

Thank you!

———

[1]Unrau, Y., & Grinnell, R.M., Jr. (2005). *Chatham-Kent Children's Services (CKCS) Help-Seeking Project for Adolescents in Out-of-Home Placement: A Research Proposal.* Submitted to Provincial Centre of Excellence for Child and Youth Mental Health at CHEO. Ottawa, Ontario, Canada K1H 8L1

APPENDIX G

(Institutional Review Board approval, if required)

Your consent forms (Appendix E) and your assent forms (Appendix F) were included in your research proposal that you sent to your college/university's institutional review board (IRB). Once your proposal is approved by the IRB, an official copy of their letter of approval is placed in Appendix G. Keep the original copy in a safe place. Read all the stipulations on the letter such as expiry dates and the like. Pay close attention to these dates.

Appendix G is left blank in the research proposal you send to your university/college's IRB because they have yet to approve your proposed study. In addition to the IRB's approval for your proposal, Appendix G should also contain additional IRB approvals from the agencies you will be using for your study.

Find out if your university/college's IRB requires any special forms or permissions that you will need to actually implement your proposed study. Box G provides a short example of how a Ph.D. student addressed the process of obtaining her university's IRB approva

---

BOX G

Example of a Research Proposal That Addressed Institutional Review Board Issues

Students' Persistence in the University of Nebraska at Lincoln: A Mixed Methods Study[1]

RESEARCH PERMISSION AND ETHICAL CONSIDERATIONS

Ethical issues will be addressed at each phase in the study. In compliance with the regulations of the Institutional Review Board (IRB), the permission for conducting the research must be obtained (Institutional Review Board). The Request for Review Form will be filed, providing information about the principal investigator, the project title and type, source of funding, type of review requested, number and type of subjects.

Application for research permission will contain the description of the project and its significance, methods and procedures, participants, and research status. This project will be accorded an expedited-middle status, since the interviews with the participants will be audio taped, though the study will be conducted in a normal social setting, its topic does not fall in the sensitive category, and the subject population is over age nineteen.

An informed consent form will be developed. The form will state that the participants are guaranteed certain rights, agree to be involved in the study, and acknowledge their rights are protected. A statement relating to informed consent will be affixed to the web survey and reflect compliance by participation.

The anonymity of participants will be protected by numerically coding each returned questionnaire and keeping the responses confidential. While conducting the individual interviews with the selected respondents, they will be assigned fictitious names for use in their description and reporting the results.

All study data, including the survey electronic files, interview tapes, and transcripts, will be kept in locked metal file cabinets in the researcher's office and destroyed after a reasonable period of time. Participants will be told summary data will be disseminated to the professional community, but in no way it will be possible to trace responses to individuals.

---

[1]Ivankova, N.V. (2002). *Students' persistence in the University of Nebraska at Lincoln: A mixed methods study.* Doctoral dissertation proposal submitted for partial fulfillment of the requirements for the degree of Doctor of Philosophy. Graduate College at the University of Nebraska at Lincoln.

APPENDIX H

(Instructions given to research participants, if applicable)

Appendix H is where you clearly delineate the instructions you will provide your research participants when it comes to filling out the measuring instruments. Sometimes the instructions for completing measuring instruments are contained within the measuring instruments themselves. Since copies of the measuring instruments are contained in Appendix D, you can simply refer the reader to that location for instructions on how to complete the measuring instruments in addition to copies of the measuring instruments themselves.

In the simplest of terms, Appendix H contains the verbal and written information given to research participants on how to fill out the measuring instruments that you did not describe in Section 8d, on data collection. You will need to include Appendix H in the research proposal you submit to your university/college's institutional review board (IRB) because they will be very concerned with how your research participants are going to be instructed on completing your measuring instruments. Sometimes this information is contained in the Informed Consent/Assent Form.

Obviously you will not need Appendix H if you do not use human research participants in your proposed study.

APPENDIX I

(Interview protocols, if needed)

Appendix I is your description of how you plan to gather information from your interviewees, assuming you are going to use interviews as a data collection method. Appendix I is another place your university/college's institutional review board (IRB) is going to scrutinize very carefully. How you plan on conducting your interviews is a very important part of the research process. Your Data Collection section, Section 8d, doesn't go into specifics of how you will specifically conduct your interviews. It will only describe the general questions you will be asking, and a copy of your interview schedule will be included in Appendix D on measuring instruments.

So, for now, just remember that Appendix I is the place where you describe exactly how you are going to conduct the interviews contained in the Appendix D interview schedule.

You will refer to Appendixes D and I in your Data Collection section. Box I is a brief example of an actual interview protocol from a research proposal.

BOX I

Example of Interview Protocols from a Research Proposal

Students' Persistence in the University of Nebraska at Lincoln: A Mixed Methods Study[1]

INTERVIEW PROTOCOLS

The Interview Protocol will include ten to fifteen open-ended questions, and will be pilot tested. The content of the protocol questions will be grounded in the results of the statistical tests of the relationships between the participants' group membership and the predictor factors as related to students' persistence in the program, and will elaborate on them.

The questions will focus on the issue of persistence in the ELHE-DE program and about the details of the cases selected on maximal variation principle. The protocol will be pilot tested on three students selected from the same target population, but then excluded from the full study.

Debriefing with the participants will be conducted to obtain information on the clarity of the interview questions and their relevance to the study aim. The participants will receive the interview questions prior to the scheduled calling time, and will be informed the interview will be tape-recorded and transcribed verbatim.

Respondents will have an opportunity to review and, if necessary, correct the contents of the interview after it has been transcribed.

---

[1]Ivankova, N.V. (2002). *Students' persistence in the University of Nebraska at Lincoln: A mixed methods study.* Doctoral dissertation proposal submitted for partial fulfillment of the requirements for the degree of Doctor of Philosophy. Graduate College at the University of Nebraska at Lincoln.

APPENDIX J

(Data collection plan)

Appendix J is not optional; it's mandatory, as it contains your specific data collection plan (and its corresponding narrative) as described in Section 8d. The table shown here and the corresponding narrative is one of many ways you can convince your readers that your data-gathering activities are not haphazard, unsystematic enterprises but well-thought-out procedures.

Example of a Data-Collection Plan for Two Variables

a	b	c	d	e	f	g
Indicator	How indicator is measured	Who provides the data	How data are gathered	When data are gathered	Where data are gathered	Who collects the data
Increase the self-esteem of pregnant adolescents after they have their babies	Rosenberg Self-Esteem Scale (Appendix D₁)	Client	1. Self-administered 2. Self-administered 3. Self-administered	1. Intake 2. Exit interview 3. 3 months after intervention	1. Waiting room 2. Social worker's office 3. Client's home	1. Receptionist 2. Social Worker 3. Case-aid
Increase the social support systems of pregnant adolescents after they have their babies	Scale of Perceived Social Support (Appendix D₂)	Client	1. Self-administered 2. Self-administered in group setting 3. Self-administered in a group setting	1. Intake 2. Last day of intervention 3. 1 month after intervention	1. Waiting room 2. In last group session 3. Group interview in coffee shop	1. Receptionist 2. Group leader 3. Research assistant

a = This column is where you list specifically what indicator(s) you are going to use to measure each one of your variables. Theoretically, you can have multiple indicators to measure the same variable.

b = This column is where you list specifically how you are going to measure each indicator in column *a*. For example, the indicators for self-esteem and social support can be measured by many different means. In our example, we chose one standardized measuring instrument for each variable: the *Rosenberg Self-Esteem Scale* for our self-esteem variable and the *Scale of Perceived Social Support* for our social support variable.

c = This column is where you list specifically who is going to provide the data, via the use of your selected measuring instrument (*b*). In a nutshell, this person, called a data source, is the one who is going to provide the data for the measuring instrument. Once again, a measuring instrument can be completed by a variety of different data sources.

d = This column is where you list specifically how the measuring instrument is going to be administered. Not only can you use a variety of measuring instruments to measure an indicator (*b*), but you also have a variety of options for how to administer them. For example, you can read the items or questions on the measuring instrument to your clients, or you can have your clients fill out the instrument themselves. You can also have clients complete them individually with no one around or in group settings such as parks, waiting rooms, and coffee shops.

e = This column is where you state the exact time frame in which the measuring instrument is going to be completed. Once again, there are many options available. For example, clients could complete measuring instruments at home on Friday nights before bedtime or at the beginning of your interview.

f = This column, which is highly related to the previous column (*e*), is where you list the specific location where the measuring instrument will be completed. For example, you can have your clients complete the *Rosenberg Self-Esteem Scale* in your program's waiting room, at home, or in your office.

g = This column is where you list specifically who is going to collect the data via the measuring instrument when it is completed. After the data source (*c*) has provided the data for the measuring instrument (*b*), who's going to collect the completed instrument for analysis? And, more importantly, who is going to collate all the data into a databank for further analyses?

APPENDIX K

(Data analysis plan)

Just as you have put together a good data collection plan, as evidenced by Appendix J, you also need to do the same for your data analysis plan. You told your readers how you specifically were going to collect the data for your variables in Appendix J. Now the time has come for you to let them know how you are going to analyze the data that you have so meticulously collected. This is done with a data analysis plan, as shown here.

Example of a Data-Analysis Plan for One Variable Measured before and after Treatment

a	b	c	d	e
Name of variable	*Name of measuring instrument*	*Measurement* level	*When data are going to be collected*	*How data are going to be analyzed*
Self-Esteem	*Index of Self-Esteem* (Appendix D_3)	Ordinal (treated as interval)	Time 1: Intake interview Time 2: Exit interview	• Descriptive statistics • One group *t*-test between Time 1 and Time 2 self-esteem scores

Many times, you will describe how your data are going to be analyzed in the body of your proposal. It doesn't hurt to provide your readers with a simple graphic of the analysis process.

APPENDIX L

(Personnel, if applicable)

Appendix L is the place where you let your reviewers know whom you plan on inviting to your party: here, you must list each and every person who will be involved in your proposed project. For each person, the following information should be included:

1. Name of person
2. Title of person, if person is based in a cooperating social work agency
3. Specific duties or roles within your project
4. Amount of involvement (e.g., part-time, hours per week)
5. Relevant experience
6. Résumé

If your proposed project involves collaboration with a social work agency, it's beneficial to present evidence of any past successful cooperation experiences you have had with the agency (see Box B in Appendix B for an example).

Tips for Writing a "Personnel" Appendix

#		Tips
212	**Yes No**	Check to see that you have obtained written permission from all persons who will be involved in your proposed research study, stating that they have read your proposal and will contribute to your project as outlined within your proposal.
213	**Yes No**	Check to see that you clarified how each person's role is essential to the success of your project and have delineated what each person will do.
214	**Yes No**	Optional: Check to see if you have spelled out exactly what your Steering Committee (Advisory Committee, Governing Board, etc.) is supposed to do in your proposed project and describe how it will be organized and who will be included.

APPENDIX M

(Résumés)

Appendix M is the place where your résumé goes. Each person who will be involved in your proposed project must include a résumé in this appendix. Unlike Appendix D where you have a separate appendix for each measuring instrument, you can group all the résumés together in Appendix M. Your readers have to know who you are, and this is where they will be able to see your research interests and qualifications.

APPENDIX N

(Dissemination plan, if applicable)

Appendix N is the location of your dissemination plan. A *dissemination plan* is simply a way to show how you will share with other audiences the information that was derived from your project. Most funding agencies are interested in seeing how their financial support of your project will extend to other audiences besides yourself. Dissemination could be done through newsletters, workshops, radio broadcasts, presentations, printed handouts, slide shows, training programs, or publications. If you have an advisory group involved with your project, they can be very helpful in disseminating your study's results to other audiences.

APPENDIX O

(Budget)

Your proposal's budget is contained in the final appendix. None of your budget items should surprise your reviewers. Furthermore, all project financial needs must be itemized in detail as well as justified in the narrative component of your budget section.

Do not pad your budget! It should only be your best-guess estimate of what your project is going to cost if it is actually going to be implemented. Nevertheless, it has to be a fairly truthful estimate. A realistic estimate of your project's costs is a good indication of your managerial ability. It's also unlikely that a funding agency will, upon the award, increase your proposed budget. There is a general tendency for students to underestimate costs (and time), so be as realistic as you can. Unforeseen circumstances will inevitably increase your costs and take more of your time than you have budgeted for.

If you will be submitting your proposal to a funding agency such as those listed on www.grants.gov, you must include a budget for your proposed study. List what equipment you need (e.g., computer, software, interviewers, travel, tape or video recorder) as well as the kind of services you will have to pay for (e.g., transcription, photocopying, binding, postage, library loans). Different funding agencies each have their own interpretations of what they will permit and ultimately fund. Thus, you will obviously have to adapt your proposal accordingly.

Funding agencies customarily specify how budgets should be presented and what costs are allowable. Your budget must show the costs that you are asking the funding agency to fund, which will include personnel, nonpersonnel, administrative, and overhead expenses. Your budget should also contain items paid for by other funding agencies, if applicable.

At all costs (no pun intended), make your budget realistic. Sharpen your pencil, or the person who will be reading your proposal will sharpen it for you—probably too sharp! Carefully think through exactly what you will need to carry out your proposed project, and establish your budget around this amount. Have fellow students and your instructor review your budget to see how realistic you are. Incorporate their suggestions, if possible.

Here are a few general categories you may need address when preparing your budget.

A. Personnel

- Principal investigator, co-principal investigator
- Graduate students
- Undergraduate students
- Professional assistants (e.g., interviewers, coders)

B. Fringe Benefits

- Personnel retirement, worker's compensation, medical/dental/life insurances, Medicare, etc.
- Graduate student tuition

C. Consultant Fees

- Honorarium
- Transportation (air, ground)
- Per diem

D. Equipment

E. Materials and Supplies

F. Travel (e.g., local, out of state)

- Transportation (e.g., air, ground)
- Per diem

G. Other

- Communications (telephone, postage)
- Shipping, courier
- Printing and duplicating
- Equipment maintenance
- Other (with explanation)